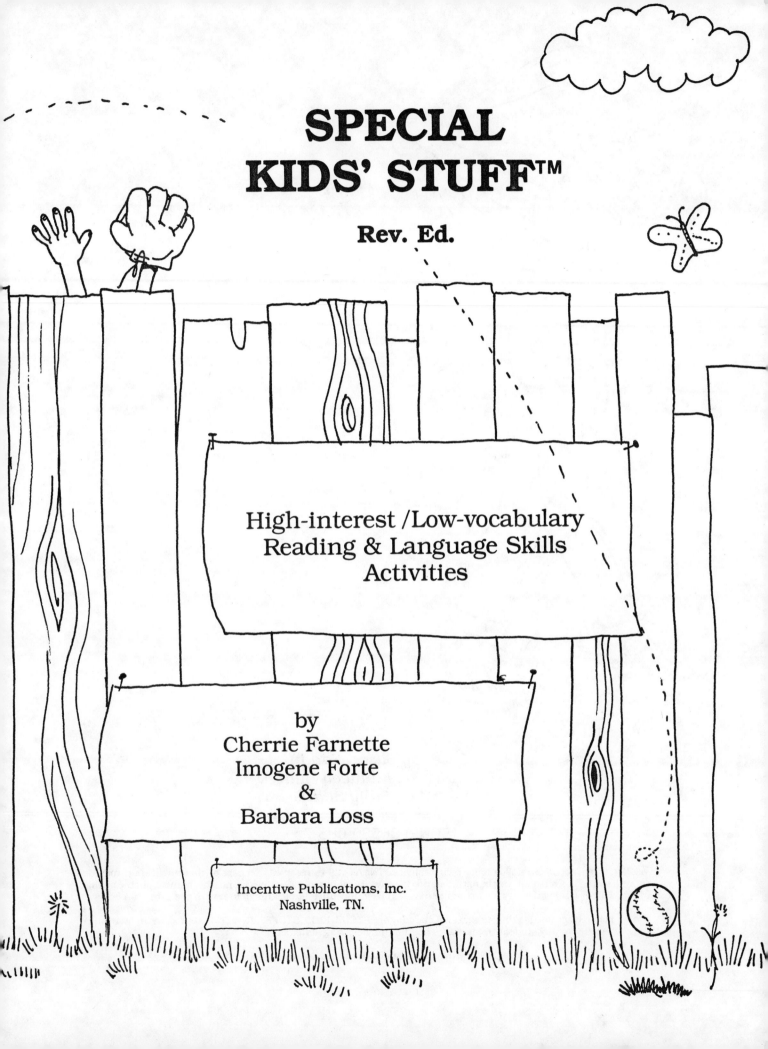

SPECIAL KIDS' STUFF™

Rev. Ed.

High-interest /Low-vocabulary
Reading & Language Skills
Activities

by
Cherrie Farnette
Imogene Forte
&
Barbara Loss

Incentive Publications, Inc.
Nashville, TN.

Cover by Susan Eaddy
Illustrated by Kathleen Bullock
Edited by Sally Sharpe

ISBN 0-86530-088-7

Table of Contents

Preface ix

WORD RECOGNITION & USAGE

Vowel Mixer
(*Using Vowel Sounds*) 13

Sound Off
(*Using Consonant Sounds & Blends*) 19

Dizzy Descriptions
(*Descriptive Words*) 25

Homonym Review
(*Using Homonyms*) 29

Moving On
(*Verb Usage*) 35

Name Dropping
(*Using Nouns & Pronouns*) 41

Perfect Ending
(*Using Suffixes*) 45

Prefix Preview
(*Using Prefixes*) 51

Rhyme Match
(*Using Rhyming Words*) 57

Word Hook-Up
(*Compound Word Usage*) 63

COMPREHENSION

Classification Turn-About
(*Classification*) 69

Context Connections
(Using Context Clues). 75

Double Talk
(Mental Imagery). 79

Hear Ye! Hear Ye!
(Critical Listening) 83

Non-Sensational
(Making Value Judgments) 87

Next Step
(Sequencing) 95

Pict-O-Gram
(Picture-Word Associations) 99

Question Box
(Critical Reading) 107

Reader's Choice
(Analogies) 113

Riddle Roundup
(Making Inferences) 119

State Your Position
(Using Position Words). 123

WORK STUDY SKILLS

Alphabet Annie
(Alphabetizing). 129

Computer Match
(Organizing Information) 135

Concrete Charlie's Correction Corner
(Punctuation & Word Usage). 141

Direction Detection
  (Following Directions) 145

If True, Do
  (Decision Making) 151

Reference Referral
  (Using Reference Materials) 157

Schedule Schemers
  (Making Schedules) 163

Shopping Center
  (Problem Solving) 167

ENRICHMENT & APPRECIATION

Detail Discovery
  (Detail Awareness) 175

Home Sweet Home
  (Idea Association) 181

Imagi-Station
  (Creative Thinking) 185

Job Market
  (Career Awareness) 193

Pop-Ins
  (Vocabulary Development) 199

Tall Tales
  (Creative Expression) 203

What's Your Line?
  (Dialogue Development) 207

World Of Words
  (Creative Word Usage) 211

APPENDIX
Terrific Puzzles To Teach Reading & Language Arts Skills

A Wordy Path 218

Crossword Calendar. 219

Crossword Opposites. 220

Daffy Definitions. 221

Delightful Days 222

Find The Words. 223

Money Mix-Up 224

Ready, Set, Go! 225

Scrambled Shopper 226

Secret Word 227

Sentence Shape-Ups 228

Word Ring-Around 229

24 Five-Minute Sparkers For Reading & Language Arts 230

Reading Record. 234

Student Interest Inventory 235

Other KIDS' STUFF™ Books For Middle Grades Language Arts
    & Reading. 236

Answer Key. 237

PREFACE

SPECIAL KIDS' STUFF is a special kind of book written for special students. It is a collection of learning experiences designed to help boys and girls use basic communication skills in a relaxed and meaningful manner. A simple unit format featuring easy-to-follow directions and limited vocabulary is utilized to introduce topics of high interest to the students. Each of the learning experiences is presented at three or more levels of difficulty to provide for differing readiness stages, skills usage and reinforcement. The three symbols below have been used to denote levels of difficulty in presentation of content and skill development.

 represents the basic knowledge level. Intellectual and creative expectancies ascend in this order: and then . The coding system will enable teachers to quickly select and adapt experiences to meet widely varying readiness stages. Students needing additional practice in a particular skill area may work through the entire set of activities without stigma while other students move on to related enrichment activities.

Teachers and students will enjoy working together to devise both teacher-directed and independent study projects, contracts or unit objectives unique to individual student needs and interests. In some instances, it may be desirable to allow students complete freedom to work through as many of the activities in a given set as time permits and/or interest is maintained. Other situations may call for a diagnostic-prescriptive approach. For example, in heterogeneous classroom settings, the activities may be presented to existing instructional groups and/or to especially created interest groups. Academically talented students will appreciate the humor and the opportunity for creative development afforded by many of the activities. Homogeneously grouped students with learning disabilities may profit from more teacher direction in the selection and completion of activities. In cases of severely handicapped students, teachers may find it appropriate to select activities to be presented in a one-to-one tutorial setting. Teachers concerned with meeting the needs of students with varying ability levels in the regular classroom will find the high-interest/low-vocabulary activities extremely valuable.

The authors of SPECIAL KIDS' STUFF believe that all kids are special. This book is an outgrowth of that belief and of the desire to contribute in some measure to the joy of learning for special kids and special teachers.

Note: Answers for all pages labeled " *Answer Key" may be found on pages 237-239.

WORD
RECOGNITION
& USAGE

VOWEL MIXER

Skills Purpose:
Using Vowel Sounds

Unit Objectives:
After completing this unit, students should be able to:
1. select vowels to complete words.
2. add "e" to words to change short vowel sounds to long vowel sounds.
3. identify words with long vowel sounds.

Preparation & Procedure:
1. Reproduce the activity sheets and provide the students with pencils and art supplies.
2. Verbally introduce the unit and explain the directions for each activity.
3. Arrange to give guidance and assistance and to aid in ongoing evaluation.
4. Make provision for filing or displaying the completed activities.

The phrases below are from recipe directions.
Circle the correct word to complete each direction by using the hint at the end of each
    line.

1. Use one   cup   of sugar. (Hint: a word with a "u" like in duck.)
             cube

2. Use   ripe   fruit. (Hint: a word with an "i" like in pie.)
           picked

3. Bake   it for twenty minutes. (Hint: a word with an "a" like in make.)
    Pat

4. Pour   hot   juice over the duck. (Hint: a word with an "o" like in box.)
           orange

5. Pot   the corn over hot fire. (Hint: a word with an "o" like in bone.)
    Roast

6. Heat   the chicken parts. (Hint: a word with an "e" like in feed.)
    Wet

7. Chop the   cheese   well. (Hint: a word with an "e" like in fed.)
           egg

8. Place the   cake   in a pan. (Hint: a word with an "a" like in fat.)
           ham

9. Use   a large piece of meat. (Hint: a word with a "u" like in pure.)
    Cut

10. Use fresh   limes   . (Hint: a word with an "i" like in fix.)
           milk

*Answer Key

Someone took everything out of the kitchen cabinet.
Place the above items back in the cabinet by writing each name on the
   proper shelf.

1.	Items that have the "a" sound as in ham.
2.	Items that have the "e" sound as in hen.
3.	Items that have the "i" sound as in pig.
4.	Items that have the "o" sound as in mop.
5.	Items that have the "u" sound as in duck.

*Answer Key

Using vowel sounds
© 1989 by Incentive Publications, Inc., Nashville, TN.

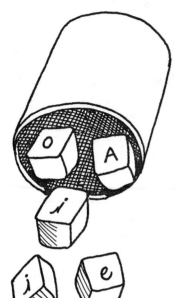

A. Complete these words by writing the missing vowels in the blanks.

1. m __ st
2. pr __ tty
3. s __ y
4. th __ s
5. h __ m
6. sh __ w
7. __ ld
8. w __
9. __ m
10. br __ wn
11. bl __ ck
12. wh __ te
13. h __ r
14. m __ ch
15. j __ mp
16. h __ d
17. c __ rry

18. l __ ng
19. h __ rt
20. h __ m
21. tw __
22. b __
23. __ r
24. w __ lk
25. br __ ng
26. k __ nd
27. wh __ t
28. th __ m
29. tr __
30. h __ lp
31. st __ p
32. h __
33. __ p

B. See how many words you can make by adding different vowels to these incomplete words.

1. n __ w
2. s __ w
3. w __ nt
4. w __ sh
5. th __ nk
6. __ t

7. w __ ll
8. b __ t
9. g __ t
10. t __ p
11. h __ m
12. __ s

13. c __ t
14. f __ ll
15. gr __ w
16. __ n
17. p __ t
18. f __ r

19. h __ ld
20. t __ n
21. b __ g
22. sh __ ll
23. w __ n
24. m __

*Answer Key

Using vowel sounds
© 1989 by Incentive Publications, Inc., Nashville, TN.

Rewrite each sentence by adding an "e" to the end of the underlined word.
This will change the short vowel to a long vowel sound and will make a new word.
Then circle the sentence which best describes the picture.

1. Bill put on his <u>cap</u>.

   _____

2. Sally put a bandage on her <u>cut</u> finger.

   _____

3. Please, don't <u>mop</u> around my desk.

   _____

4. He walked with a <u>can</u> in his hand.

   _____

5. <u>Tap</u> your foot on the floor.

   _____

6. Tom's baby brother was left in his <u>car</u>.

   _____

7. It was his <u>fat</u> that got him into trouble.

   _____

8. <u>Tim</u> flies.

   _____

Using vowel sounds
© 1989 by Incentive Publications, Inc., Nashville, TN.

Rewrite the story in the space below.
Add the missing vowels.

Th__ l__st d__y of sch ____l is a h __ppy

d__y. Th__ s__mm__r m__nths __re h__ppy

d __ys of pl __y and no sch ____lw __rk.

St __d__nts w__sh v__c __t__on c____ld

l __st __ll ye __r, b __t aft__r a l __ng

s __mm __r th __y s __em gl __d to g __t

b __ck to th__ b____ks.

_____

_____

_____

_____

_____

_____

_____

_____

_____

_____

Using vowel sounds
© 1989 by Incentive Publications. Inc., Nashville. TN.

SOUND OFF

Skills Purpose:
Using Consonant Sounds and Blends

Unit Objectives:
After completing this unit, students should be able to:
1. identify consonant sounds.
2. supply consonant sounds to complete words.
3. supply consonant blends to complete words used in context.

Preparation & Procedure:
1. Reproduce the activity sheets and provide the students with pencils and crayons. Prepare a bulletin board display titled "Sound-Off" and border it with consonant letters and blends cut from multi-colored construction paper.
2. Verbally introduce the activities.
3. Ask the students to work together in groups of three to complete the activities. Arrange time blocks to allow for the "fun" discussion that should be an important part of this unit.
4. Allow time for guidance and ongoing evaluation.
5. Make provision for filing the completed activities.

19

Name the pictures in each box.
Mark the three pictures in each box that have the same beginning sound.

Using consonant sounds & blends
© 1989 by Incentive Publications, Inc., Nashville, TN.

Fill in these missing letters to complete the story.

b-   p-   g-   or   f-

There was a __asketball __layer named __aul who __ave the __ame his all. He had only one __ault, and that was a shame. He brought a __ootball to the __asketball __ame. When he tossed the __ootball in the __asket, he lost the __ame as well as his __ame.

Circle the words in the story that rhyme with "same."

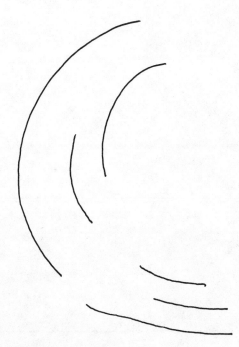

Use the word endings to complete this story.

| -ug | -ig | or | -ag |

There was a b⎯, ugly b⎯⎯ who lived in a paper b⎯⎯. He jumped out of the b⎯⎯, ran over a dish r⎯⎯ and fell on the r⎯⎯. Don't you wish you could be as happy as that b⎯⎯, ugly b⎯⎯ so sn⎯⎯ in the r⎯⎯?

Write a poem in the space below.

Use these words:

pig	tag	dug
wig	wag	tug

Use these letter combinations to complete the words
in this story.

 th   dr   or   ck

___in, ___irsty Ru___ found the pa___ to the Sna____
Sha____ owned by Ja____ . By the time she got
___ere, her mou___ was so ____y ___at she
ordered ___ree ___ings to ___ink. She also asked
for ____ree more ___ings to put in her sa___ for an
afternoon sna____ .

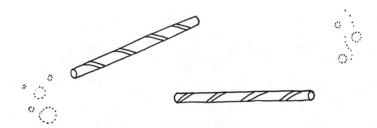

List three things that Ruth could have in her snack sack.

1. _____

2. _____

3. _____

Use these letter combinations to complete the questions below.

        or

sh-   ch-   sw-   scr-   bl-   cr-   cl-   qu-   or   fr-

Have you heard:

_____ickens _____ucking?

_____uebirds _____irping?

_____ogs _____oaking?

_____imming ducks _____acking?

_____eep _____eating?

hungry babies _____ying?

_____ildren _____outing and _____eaming?

Using consonant sounds & blends
© 1989 by Incentive Publications, Inc., Nashville, TN.

DIZZY DESCRIPTIONS

Skills Purpose:
Descriptive Words

Unit Objectives:
After completing this unit, students should be able to:
1. use descriptive words with understanding.
2. associate descriptive words with pictures and emotions.
3. use descriptive words in sentence construction.

Preparation & Procedure:
1. Reproduce the activity sheets.
2. Provide motivation and develop readiness for the unit by discussing the use of descriptive words and how they make speaking and writing more interesting.
3. Explain the activities to enable the students to work as independently as possible.
4. Allow time for evaluation of the completed activities.
5. Make provision for filing or displaying the completed activities.

NAME _____

Fill the hand with words that describe the way things feel to the touch.

Write a descriptive word for each of these things:

sandpaper _____   kitten _____

cotton _____   broken glass _____

wet rock _____   rain _____

knife _____   paper bag _____

glue _____   marshmallow _____

Descriptive words
© 1989 by Incentive Publications, Inc., Nashville, TN.

Write words that describe feelings in the blanks below.

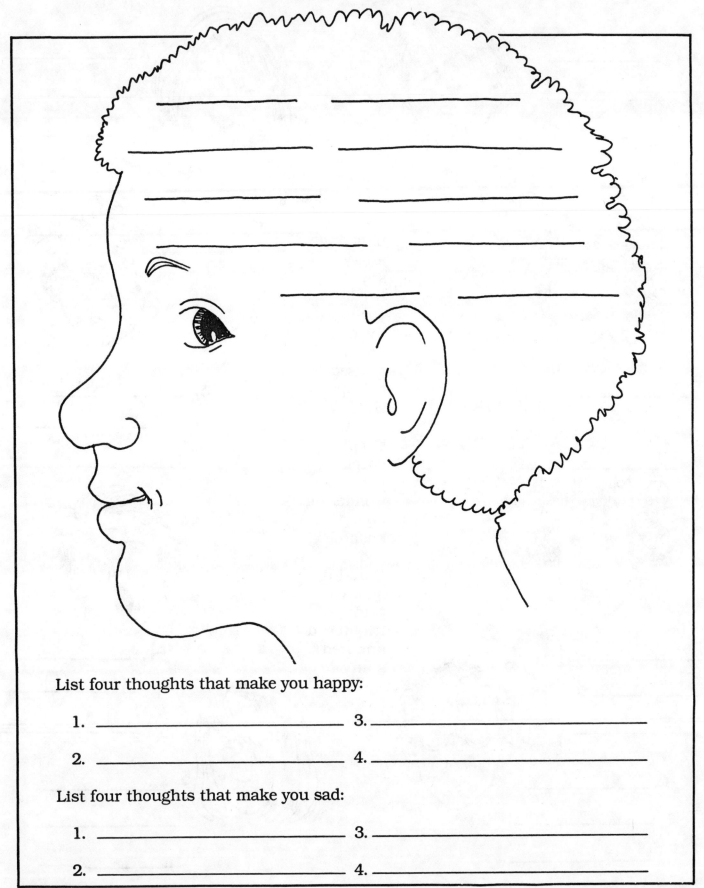

List four thoughts that make you happy:

1. _____   3. _____

2. _____   4. _____

List four thoughts that make you sad:

1. _____   3. _____

2. _____   4. _____

1. _____
   _____
   _____

2. _____
   _____
   _____

Match each word to the correct picture.
Write each word next to the face it best describes.

blushing
angry
shy
tired
surprised
furious
bored
pleased
unhappy
sly
questioning
sleepy
sneaky
happy
wondering
crying
bashful
sad
thinking
shocked
glad
frightened
annoyed
shifty

8. _____
   _____
   _____

3. _____
   _____
   _____

7. _____
   _____
   _____

4. _____
   _____
   _____

6. _____
   _____
   _____

5. _____
   _____
   _____

Descriptive words
© 1989 by Incentive Publications, Inc., Nashville, TN.

*Answer Key

HOMONYM REVIEW

Skills Purpose:

Using Homonyms

Unit Objectives:

After completing this unit, students should be able to:
1. recognize words that sound alike but have different meanings.
2. use homonyms meaningfully.
3. use homonyms to express creative thoughts.

Preparation & Procedure:
1. Reproduce the activity sheets. Provide the students with pencils, dictionaries, construction paper and crayons.
2. Verbally introduce the unit.
3. Allow time for discussion and ongoing evaluation of each activity.
4. Make provision for sharing the completed activity sheets in a small group setting.
5. Ask the students to use construction paper to make folders for their completed activity sheets.

Optional Follow-Up Activity:
1. Have the students write sentences using the words not used in the sentences on page 34.

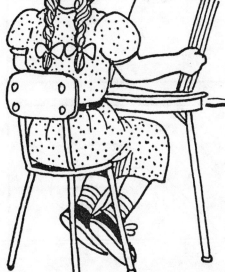

Circle the word pictured in each box.
Write a sentence using the circled word.

knows
nose

1. _____

8

ate
eight

2. _____

2

two
too
to

3. _____

$4 + 5 = ?$

sum
some

4. _____

flower
flour

5. _____

sew
so

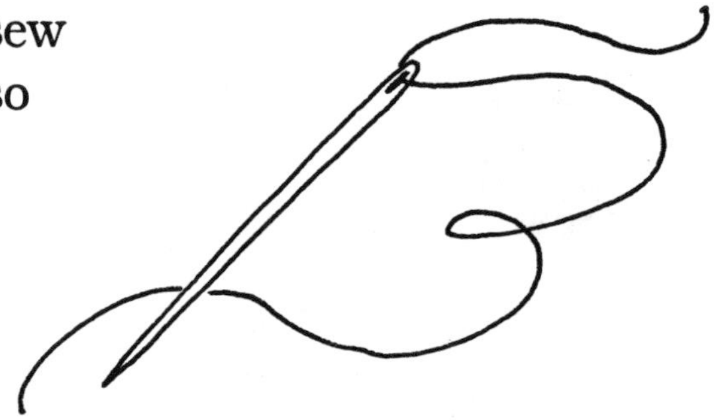

6. _____

Using homonyms
© 1989 by Incentive Publications, Inc., Nashville, TN.

Circle the word pictured in each box.
Write a sentence using the circled word.

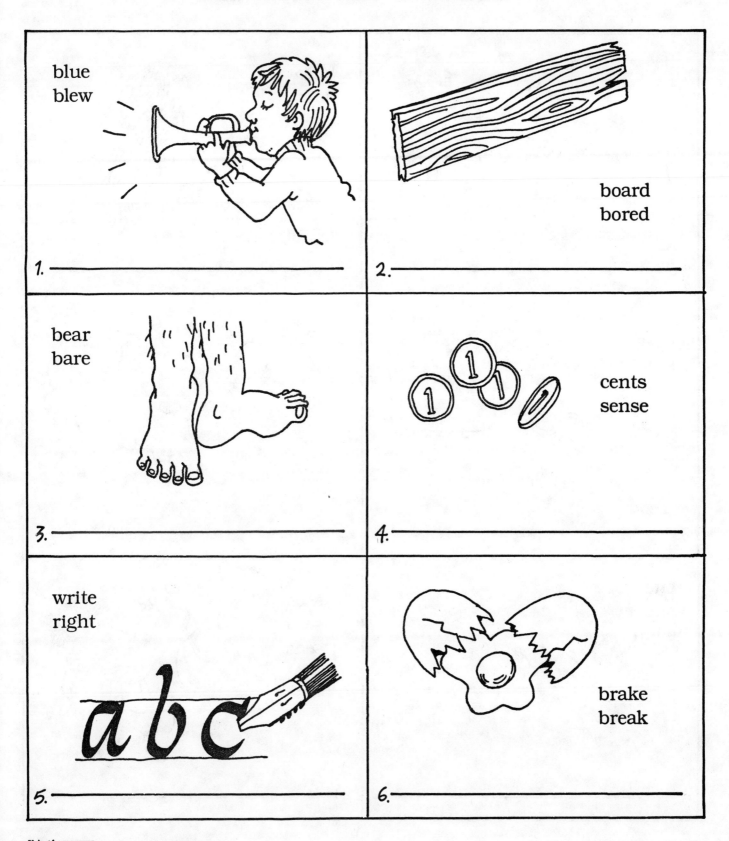

blue
blew

1. _____

board
bored

2. _____

bear
bare

3. _____

cents
sense

4. _____

write
right

5. _____

brake
break

6. _____

Circle the word pictured in each box.
Write a sentence using the circled word.

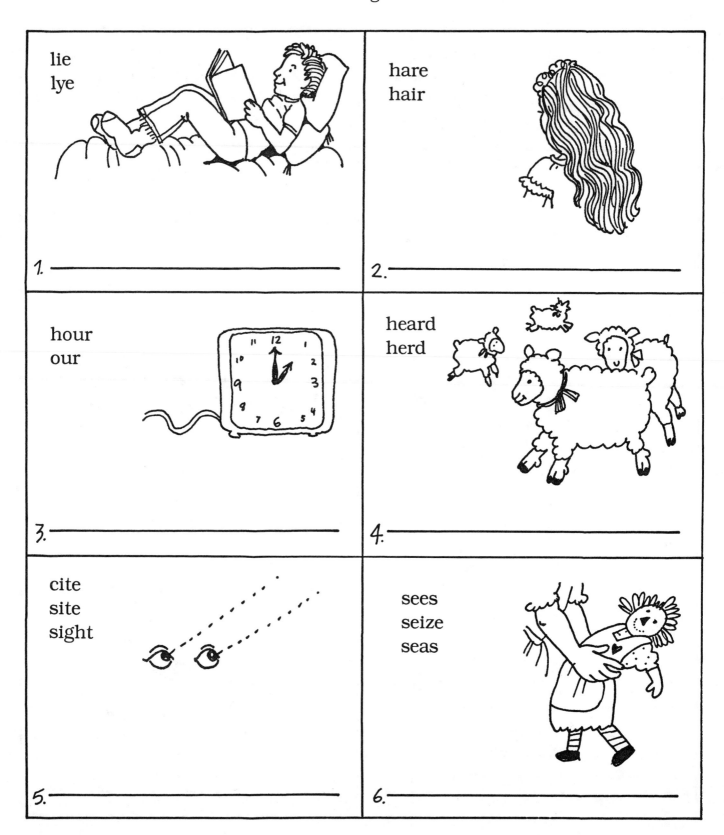

lie
lye

1. _____

hare
hair

2. _____

hour
our

3. _____

heard
herd

4. _____

cite
site
sight

5. _____

sees
seize
seas

6. _____

Using homonyms
© 1989 by Incentive Publications. Inc., Nashville. TN.

Find these words in the puzzle and circle them:

an	tall	like
too	two	toe
to	look	not

A. Circle the correct word to complete each sentence.

1. I went (to, too, two) the zoo.
2. I have (to, too, two) hands.
3. I ate (to, too, two) much candy.

B. Complete this story by writing the correct word in each
    blank — TO, TOO, or TWO.
1. I went _____ the store _____ buy _____ apples.
2. The grocer gave four apples _____ me.
3. I told him that he gave _____ many apples _____ me.
4. He gave me _____ more than the _____ apples I wanted
    _____ buy.

Using homonyms
© 1989 by Incentive Publications, Inc., Nashville, TN.

*Answer Key

33

Choose the correct word for each sentence.

1. The story was written _____ Mark Twain.
   (by, buy)

2. Roy _____ his friend.
   (seas, sees, seize)

3. Tom goes _____ school.
   (to, two, too)

4. Did you ever see a big brown _____ asleep in a bed?
   (bare, bear)

5. All of our friends are _____ .
   (hear, here)

6. The _____ for the race was a rough one.
   (course, coarse)

7. Jan _____ the bed.
   (made, maid)

8. The kittens' _____ to come inside were ignored.
   (please, pleas)

9. Joe and Tom went to _____ home.
   (there, their, they're)

10. Jack went fishing with his rod and _____ .
    (real, reel)

11. There were _____ pieces of cake left on the plate.
    (four, for)

12. It was Jill's turn to _____ the drum.
    (beet, beat)

13. Tony needed to repair the emergency _____ on his car.
    (break, brake)

14. The _____ of the new shopping center was on the corner.
    (cite, site, sight)

15. Bob was so _____ that he fell asleep.
    (board, bored)

Using homonyms
© 1989 by Incentive Publications, Inc., Nashville, TN.

MOVING ON

Skills Purpose:
Verb Usage

Unit Objectives:
After completing this unit, students should be able to:
1. use action words correctly.
2. change verbs from present to past tense.
3. use verbs creatively to express original thoughts.

Preparation & Procedure:
1. Reproduce the activity sheets. Provide the students with pencils, dictionaries and extra paper.
2. Verbally introduce the unit, and devote as much time as necessary to the development of students' understanding of verbs and their usage.
3. Let the students work in pairs to complete the activities and to "check" each other's completed work.
4. Make provision for filing or displaying the completed activity sheets.

Optional Follow-up Activities:
1. Encourage the students to compare their word lists (page 36).
2. Ask each student to write another action verb for each picture on page 37.
3. Instruct the students to repeat the activity on page 39, this time changing the verbs to future tense.

35

Look at the picture carefully.
Discuss with a friend what is happening in the picture.
List five action words that can be used to describe what is happening in the picture.

Action Words

1. _____

2. _____

3. _____

4. _____

5. _____

❖ NAME ______________________________

Write an action word to complete each sentence.
Rewrite each sentence and change the verbs to past tense.

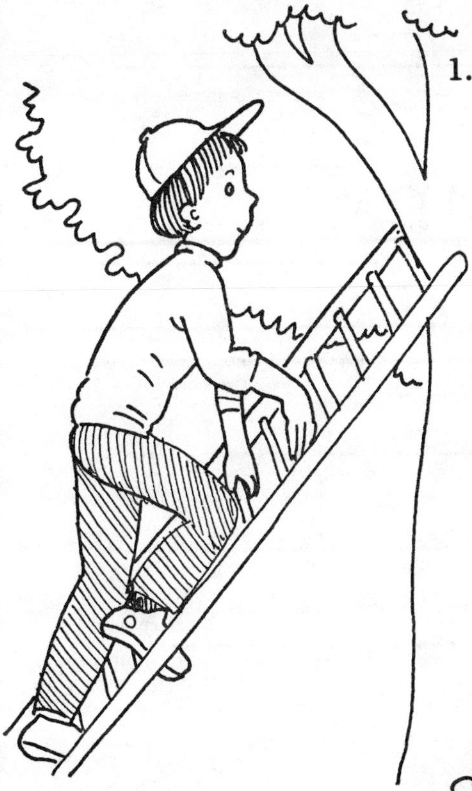

1. He is ____________________.

____

____

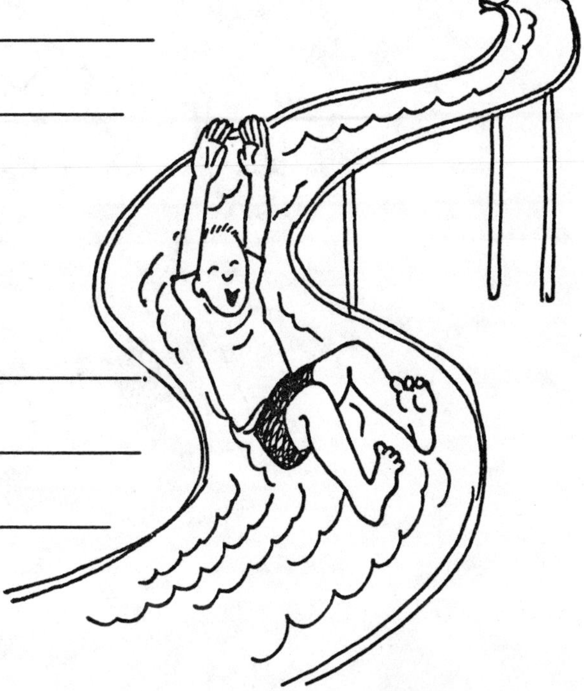

2. He is ____________________.

____

____

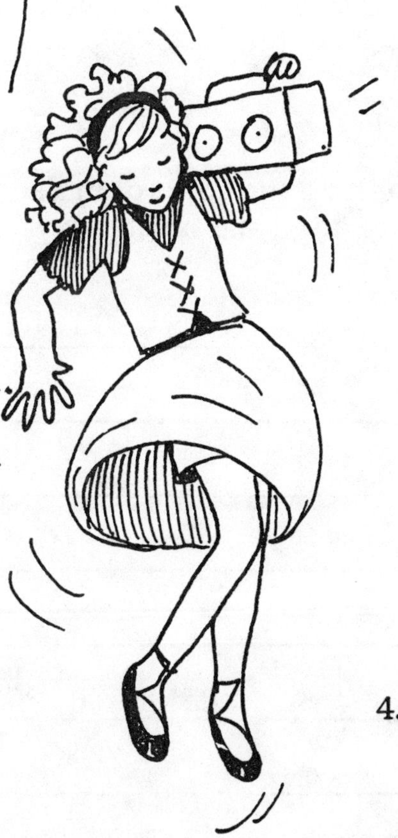

3. She is ____________________.

____

____

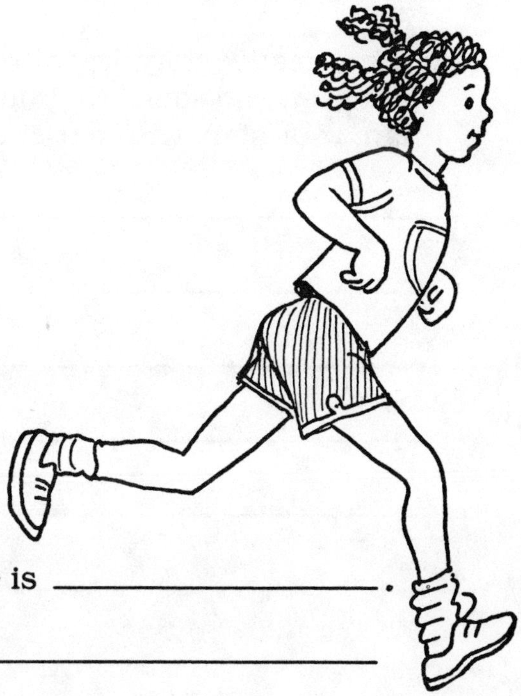

4. She is ____________________.

____

____

Verb usage

Write an action word on each line below.

1. _____

2. _____

3. _____

4. _____

5. _____

6. _____

7. _____

8. _____

Write a creative story describing something the boy is doing, something he did in
   the past, and something he plans to do in the future.
Share your story with a friend.

_____

_____

_____

_____

_____

_____

_____

_____

_____

Read each sentence to a friend.
Ask the friend to change the verb to past tense and to repeat the sentence.
The verbs are underlined and the correct answer is given at the end of each
sentence.

Example: You say, "John walks."
             Your friend should say, "John walked."

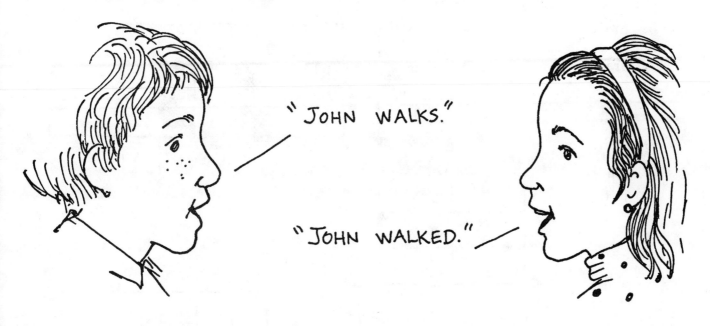

1. Sue talks. (Sue talked.)
2. Tim jumps. (Tim jumped.)
3. Joe hops. (Joe hopped.)
4. Bob plays ball. (Bob played ball.)
5. Barbara watches television. (Barbara watched television.)
6. Mary listens to Jane. (Mary listened to Jane.)
7. Sam carries the box. (Sam carried the box.)
8. Jason eats bread. (Jason ate bread.)
9. Tom sits on the chair. (Tom sat on the chair.)
10. Jennifer runs to school. (Jennifer ran to school.)
11. David comes to supper. (David came to supper.)
12. Jean sees the book. (Jean saw the book.)
13. Sally writes a letter. (Sally wrote a letter.)
14. Henry goes to the show. (Henry went to the show.)

Verb usage
© 1989 by Incentive Publications, Inc., Nashville, TN.

Change each verb from the present tense to the past tense.
Write the past tense of each verb in the correct puzzle boxes.

Across:
2. bring
5. find
6. lead
7. are
8. pay

Down:
1. sell
3. get
4. tell
7. weep

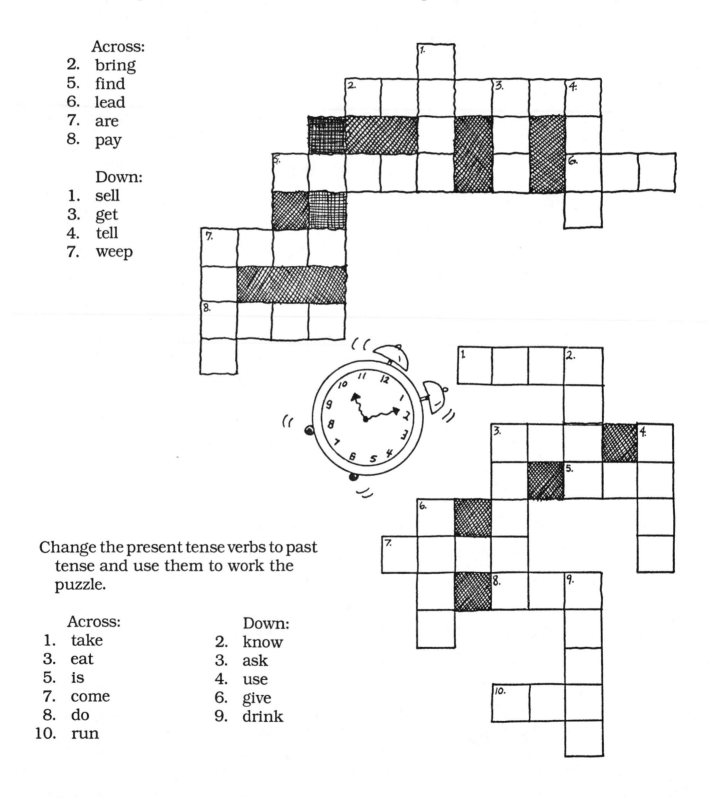

Change the present tense verbs to past
tense and use them to work the
puzzle.

Across:
1. take
3. eat
5. is
7. come
8. do
10. run

Down:
2. know
3. ask
4. use
6. give
9. drink

Verb usage
© 1989 by Incentive Publications, Inc., Nashville, TN.

*Answer Key

NAME DROPPING

Skills Purpose:
Using Nouns and Pronouns

Unit Objectives:
After completing this unit, students should be able to:
1. recognize and use nouns.
2. recognize and use pronouns.
3. use possessive pronouns.

Preparation & Procedure:
1. Reproduce the activity sheets and provide the students with pencils and dictionaries.
2. Verbally introduce the unit and review the definitions for nouns and pronouns and the rules related to their use.
3. Encourage the students to complete the activities as independently as possible. Provide time for ongoing guidance and evaluation.
4. Encourage the students to take home their completed activity sheets to share with family members or friends.

41

Look at the pictures.
Write the noun which names each picture in the correct puzzle boxes.

Nouns to use:

book
table
chair
bear
car
bird
pencil
horse
ball
girl
boy

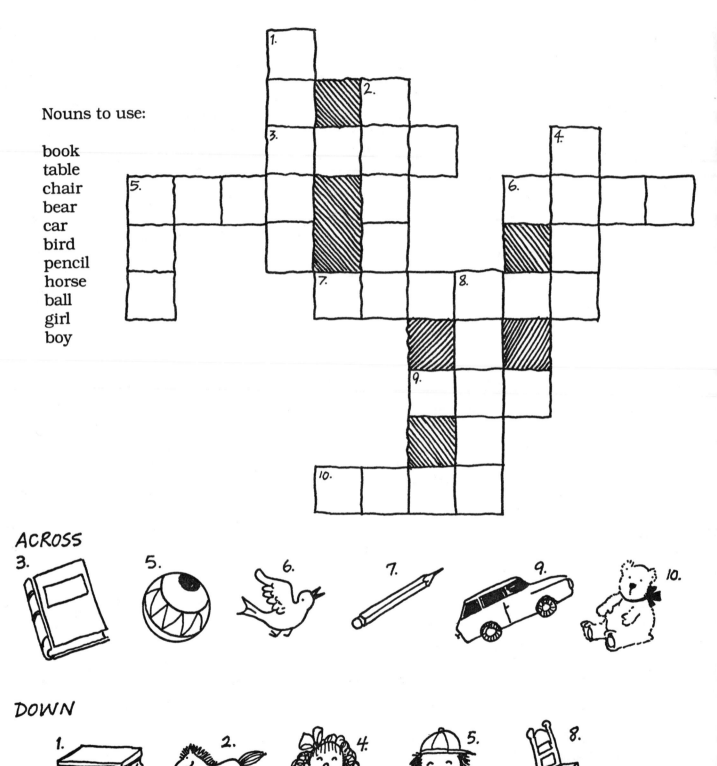

ACROSS

3. 5. 6. 7. 9. 10.

DOWN

1. 2. 4. 5. 8.

*Answer Key

Find these pronouns in this puzzle and circle them.

he	I	she	this
hers	it	them	you
his	mine	they	

Y	I	T	H	E	M
O	T	H	I	S	I
U	H	E	R	S	N
S	M	Y	S	H	E

Complete each sentence with the correct pronoun from the puzzle.

1. I love y __ __ .

2. This towel is hers. This one is h __ __ .

3. That bicycle is yours. This one is m __ __ __ .

4. They went to the party. I went with t __ __ __ .

5. He wears shirts. S __ __ wears skirts.

6. That book is yours. T __ __ __ one is mine.

7. She is a girl. H __ is a boy.

8. The boys went to the movies. T __ __ __ had a good time.

9. __ love you.

10. The blue car is his. The pink one is h __ __ __ .

11. I lost my hat. Do you know where i __ is?

Using nouns & pronouns
© 1989 by Incentive Publications, Inc., Nashville, TN.

*Answer Key

Find the correct pronoun for each blank.
Write the pronouns in the puzzle boxes.

Pronouns to use:
he   they
she   I
it   us
we   you

Across:
1. _____ (one letter meaning me)
2. _____ are talking.
5. He will see _____ .
7. _____ are working the puzzle together.

Down:
1. _____ is spring.
3. _____ is a boy.
4. _____ are working with your friend.
6. _____ is a girl.

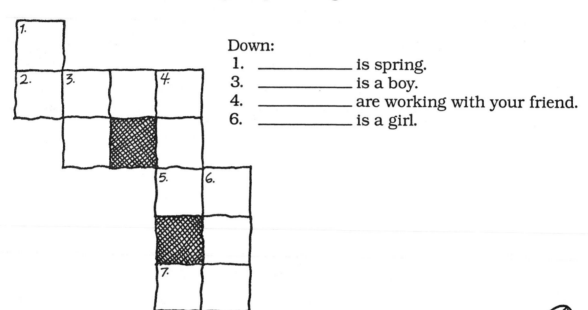

Fill in the blanks with the correct possessive pronouns.
Use the pronouns to work this puzzle.

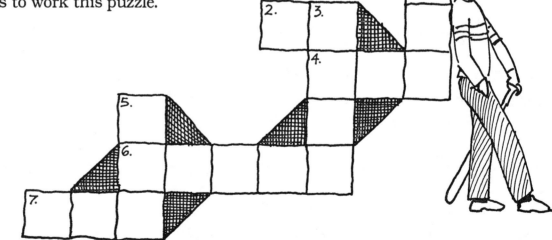

Across:
2. I use __ __ pencil.
4. We go to __ __ __ own house.
6. They go to _____ own house.
7. He reads __ __ __ own book.

Down:
1. She uses __ __ __ own pencil.
3. You use __ __ __ __ own pencil.
5. In fall, the tree loses __ __ __ leaves.

Using nouns & pronouns
© 1989 by Incentive Publications, Inc., Nashville, TN.

*Answer Key

PERFECT ENDING

Skills Purpose:
Using Suffixes

Unit Objectives:
After completing this unit, students should be able to:
1. recognize suffixes within words.
2. add suffixes to root words to make new words.
3. recognize and use root words.
4. alter story plots by changing the suffixes of given root words.

Preparation & Procedure:
1. Reproduce the activity sheets and provide the students with pencils and dictionaries.
2. Verbally introduce the unit, giving examples and explaining the instructions for each activity.
3. Allow time for ongoing evaluation and give reinforcement as needed.
4. Make provision for sharing the completed activities in a small group setting.

Optional Follow-up Activities:
1. Ask each student to write and illustrate a story about someone who does things "backward" (page 47).
2. Have each student write a soap opera script to act out with a friend.

Help the director write an opening night "pep-talk" for the actors.
Write the correct root word and suffix in each blank.

Root words to use:
power
success
happy
care
dark
act
wonder
kind
help

Suffixes:
-ness (the state of being)
-ful (full of)
-ors (ones who)

It will be a _____ day for all of the _____.
1. (full of wonder)   2. (ones who act)

Be _____ to learn your lines. Be _____ to the
3. (full of care)   4. (full of help)

other _____ .
5. (ones who act)

When the lights are out, be _____ not to fall in the
6. (full of care)

_____ . Be _____ to the _____ .
7. (state of being dark)   8. (full of help)   9. (ones who act)

_____ will help you find _____ .
10. (the state of being kind)   11. (the state of being happy)

I know the show will be a hit! When the play is over, you will know

what a _____ feeling it is to be _____ !
12. (full of power)   13. (full of success)

Read this story and circle the words that have the following
endings:

-est   -ward   -ed   -ing

BACKWARD MOVES

The funniest movie I ever saw was about a girl who did
all things backward. She went to bed in the morning
and got up at night. She brushed her teeth before eating
candy and washed her hands before playing with clay.
When it was raining, she waited until she was inside the
house to put on her raincoat. She read books backward
and answered the last question on a test first. She wore
her dress over her coat and her socks over her shoes.
The only thing she ever did frontward was to back up!

Write the base word for each word that you circled in the
story:

1. _____   7. _____

2. _____   8. _____

3. _____   9. _____

4. _____   10. _____

5. _____   11. _____

6. _____   12. _____

Using suffixes
© 1989 by Incentive Publications, Inc., Nashville, TN.

Rewrite this soap opera script.
Using the suffixes -ful or -less, change the ending of each underlined word so that
the script makes sense.

Mary: Oh, Charles, this is a joyless occasion. You have returned home! The time you were gone seemed endful.

Charles: Mary, my Mary, you are so thoughtless to care for my safe homecoming.

Mary: Charles, you are so fearful to travel alone to the supermarket. You are indeed a powerless person!

Charles: It was nothing. I just had to be watchless of the careful shoppers and their grocery carts.

Mary: You must be very tired. I hope you have a restless night. What can I do to be helpless?

Charles: I am thankless that I have a dutiless wife to care for me. You can bring my colorless slippers for my sore feet.

Mary: Oh, Charles, you are so good to make me feel so useless!

_____
_____
_____
_____
_____
_____
_____
_____

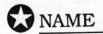 **NAME** _____

Fill in the blanks by adding the correct suffix to the word at the end of each sentence.

Write the changed word in the numbered puzzle boxes

Across:

2. Jim is always so happy and _____.(cheer)
4. The movie was full of _____ and adventure. (act)
7. The truck rolled _____ . (back)
9. Thank you for your _____ . (kind)
11. I felt so _____ when the kitten couldn't climb down the tree. (help)
12. That was a good answer for such a difficult _____ . (quest)

Down:

1. The light was so bright that we could _____ see what happened. (clear)
3. I look _____ to vacation time. (for)
5. You were very _____ to remember my birthday. (thought)
6. A power failure left the city in total _____.(dark)
8. It was very _____ of you to leave your bicycle in the street. (care)
10. She smiled _____ and left the room. (sweet)

Suffixes to use:

    -ly
    -ful
    -ward
    -ness
    -less
    -ion

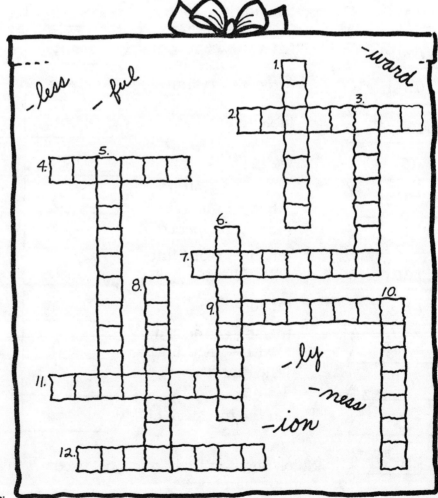

*Answer Key

SUF FIX

Word Construction

Make new words by finding a suffix for each root word.
Write the new words in the blanks provided.
Look up each new word in the dictionary and read its definition.

Root Word	Suffix Meaning	Suffix	New Word
1. pay			1.
2. drain			2.
3. front	(full of)	-ful	3.
4. clear	(act or condition)	-ion	4.
5. allow	(act of; group of)	-age	5.
6. arm	(quality; degree)	-ity	6.
7. cheer	(tends toward)	-ive	7.
8. care	(lacking)	-less	8.
9. help	(that can be)	-able	9.
10. wish	(process; amount)	-ance	10.
11. collect	(able to be)	-ible	11.
12. act	(state of)	-ness	12.
13. quest	(state or result of happening)	-ing	13.
14. like	(having happened)	-ed	14.
15. real	(changes word into an adverb)	-ly	15.
16. effect	(act of)	-ment	16.
17. fruit	(person connected with something)	-er	17.
18. ail	(one that does a thing)	-or	18.
19. fix	(in the direction of)	-ward	19.
20. sweet			20.

Note: Some suffixes may be used more than once.

Using suffixes
© 1989 by Incentive Publications, Inc., Nashville, TN.

*Answer Key

PREFIX PREVIEW

Skills Purpose:
Using Prefixes

Unit Objectives:
After completing this unit, students should be able to:
1. add prefixes to root words to make new words.
2. rewrite sentences to incorporate prefixes added to root words.
3. alter story plots by adding prefixes to root words.

Preparation & Procedure:
1. Reproduce the activity sheets. Provide the students with pencils, dictionaries, construction paper, and scissors.
2. Verbally introduce the unit, giving examples and explaining the instructions for each activity.
3. Allow time for ongoing evaluation and give reinforcement as needed.
4. Ask the students to write additional root words and prefixes on construction paper and to cut them apart and make new words (using the prefix word construction activity page as a model).
5. Make provision for sharing rewritten stories in a group setting and for filing other completed activities.

"Unlucky Andy"

Andy was <u>unhappy</u>.
She was <u>ungrateful</u> for many things.
She was <u>unhealthy</u>. Her parents were <u>unkind</u>. Her teacher was <u>unfair</u>.
Her classmates were <u>unfriendly</u>. It's <u>unbelievable</u> that a girl could be so <u>unlucky</u>!

Rewrite this story.
Turn "Unlucky Andy" into "Lucky Andy" by removing the prefix "un-" from the underlined words.

"Lucky Andy"

Using prefixes
© 1989 by Incentive Publications, Inc., Nashville, TN.

❖ NAME _____

Rewrite the sentences below.
Change the meaning of each sentence by adding prefixes to the underlined words.

Prefixes to use: trans-, out-

The baseball player planted the flower in the field.

1. _____

_____

_____

1.

Prefixes to use: un-, in-

The boy was lucky because he counted the money correctly.

2. _____

_____

_____

2.

Prefixes to use: un-, in-

He wore his shirt buttoned because the party was formal.

3. _____

_____

_____

3.

Prefixes to use: mis-, in-

When she spelled the word "right" on the test, she felt secure.

4. _____

_____

_____

4.

Using prefixes
© 1989 by Incentive Publications, Inc., Nashville, TN.

53

Rewrite the sentences below.
Add the prefixes to the underlined words.

Prefixes: tri-, de-

1. _____
_____
_____
_____

He rode his <u>cycle</u> on a <u>tour</u>.

1.

Prefixes: mis-, un-

2. _____
_____
_____
_____

Sue <u>understood</u> because she was <u>familiar</u> with the information.

2.

Prefixes: re-, non-

3. _____
_____
_____
_____

This sentence was <u>written</u> so that it makes <u>sense</u>.

3.

Prefixes: re-, ex-, uni-

4. _____
_____
_____
_____

EXCHANGES

Harry <u>turned</u> to the store to <u>change</u> his <u>cycle</u>.

4.

Prefixes: pre, in-, dis-,

5. _____
_____
_____
_____

Due to his <u>occupation</u> with <u>justice</u>, he was <u>trustful</u>.

5. SUPERIOR COURT JUDGE

Using prefixes
© 1989 by Incentive Publications, Inc., Nashville, TN.

Repete The Rebuilder

Repete the rebuilder has to redo everything. He rebuilds houses. He rehammers and renails every board. He replaces the carpets. He repaints the walls. He rehangs the wallpaper. He even replants the grass.

Repete wants to rebuild his bank account, so he reapplies to be repaid in cash before all of the work has been redone.

Would you repay Repete for all of the work he has to redo?

Rewrite the story. Change Repete's name and the way he works by leaving off the prefix "re-" every time it appears in the story.

Pete The Builder

_____

_____

_____

_____

_____

_____

_____

Using prefixes
© 1989 by Incentive Publications. Inc.. Nashville. TN.

PRE > FIX

Word Construction

Make new words by finding a prefix for each root word.
Write the new words in the blanks provided.
Look up each new word in the dictionary and read its definition.

Prefix	Meaning	Root Word	New Word
bi-	(two)	1. trust	1. _____
con-	(with)	2. view	2. _____
de-	(do the opposite)	3. cycle	3. _____
dis-	(away from)	4. lay	4. _____
en-	(to make)	5. tend	5. _____
ex-	(out of)	6. place	6. _____
in-	(within)	7. large	7. _____
mis-	(wrong)	8. joy	8. _____
non-	(not, lack of)	9. grown	9. _____
pre-	(before)	10. cite	10. _____
pro-	(forward)	11. claim	11. _____
re-	(again)	12. form	12. _____
un-	(not)	13. like	13. _____
		14. fit	14. _____
		15. take	15. _____
		16. sense	16. _____
		17. vent	17. _____
		18. part	18. _____
		19. force	19. _____
		20. tract	20. _____

Using prefixes
© 1989 by Incentive Publications, Inc., Nashville, TN.

*Answer Key

RHYME MATCH

Skills Purpose:

Using Rhyming Words

Unit Objectives:

After completing this unit, students should be able to:
1. recognize rhyming words.
2. make meaningful use of rhyming words.

Preparation & Procedure:
1. Reproduce the activity sheets. Provide the students with pencils, extra paper, and crayons.
2. Play a rhyming word game as motivation for the unit. Discuss the activity sheets and give detailed instructions for their completion.
3. Allow time for guidance and ongoing evaluation.
4. Make provision for filing the completed activities.

Name the pictures in each row.
Circle the two pictures that rhyme.

Look at the words at the bottom of the page and find a word that rhymes
   with each picture.
Write the rhyming words in the
   correct puzzle boxes.

ACROSS:

DOWN:

1.

3.

4.

6.

7.

8.

9.

1.

2.

3.

4.

5.

7.

8.

Rhyming words to use:

cat   wing
floor   hen
dog   can
mouse   fix
wag   fell
coat   dish
five   money

Using rhyming words
© 1989 by Incentive Publications, Inc., Nashville, TN.

*Answer Key

Read these rhyming stories.
Circle all of the words that rhyme in each story.
Find each short *a* and put a curved mark (˘) over the vowel.
(For example: băt, Dăn, Săm.)

1. A Fat Cat

   A fat cat
      sat on my hat.
   See how flat
      that fat cat
      made my hat!

2. Dan's Plan

   The weather was very hot.
      Daring Dan had a dopey plan.
   He bought a warm air heater
      and sold his cold air fan!

3. Sad Sam

   Mad, sad Sam
      was playing in the sand.
   He wanted to make a river,
      but all he got was land!

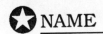

Read the rhyming stories.
Circle all of the words that rhyme in each story.
Find each short *i* and put a curved mark (˘) over the vowel.
(For example: kĭng, ĭtch.)

1. King, Sing

The king found a wishing ring.
  He wished that he could sing.
What a silly, nilly thing —
  for a king to wish to sing!

2. Witch, Stitch

There was a witch
  who liked to stitch.
She gave up her broom
  for a sewing room.

3. Pig, Wig

Dick put a big wig
  on his pink pig.
It was a perfect fit
  But the pig didn't like it . . . ONE BIT!

Using rhyming words
© 1989 by Incentive Publications, Inc., Nashville, TN.

*Answer Key

NAME

Read these rhyming stories.
Follow the directions for each story.

1. Ten In A Tent

Circle all of the words that rhyme with "Ken."
Underline the words that rhyme with "sent."
Cross out the words that rhyme with "led."
Find each short *e* and put a curved mark (˘) over the vowel.
(For example: mĕn.)

There were ten men in a crowded tent
So they went to find one to rent.
All they could find was an empty shed
So that is where five went to bed.

2. Rob's Job

Circle all of the words that rhyme with "cob."
Underline the words that rhyme with "top."
Find each short *o* and put a curved mark (˘)
over the vowel. (For example: pŏp.)
Find each long *o* and put a straight mark (-)
over the vowel. (For example: ōne.)

Pop owned a soda shop.
   He needed someone to mop.
So he hired a boy named Rob
   to do that special cleaning job.

Using rhyming words
© 1989 by Incentive Publications, Inc., Nashville, TN.

*Answer Key

WORD HOOK-UP

Skills Purpose:
Compound Word Usage

Unit Objectives:
After completing this unit, students should be able to:
1. make compound words from two words.
2. associate compound words and pictures.
3. use compound words meaningfully.

Preparation & Procedure:
1. Reproduce the activity sheets and provide the students with pencils and dictionaries.
2. Verbally introduce the unit.
3. Arrange to have conference time for discussion and evaluation of each completed activity and provide additional reinforcement as needed.
4. Make provision for filing or displaying the completed activity sheets.
5. Ask the students to use the dictionary for help in making lists of as many additional compound words as they can.

Write the correct word under each picture.
Put the two words together to make a new word.

Words to use: pan   horse   hand   fly   shoe
               bug   cup   tooth   board   brush
               bag   lady   cake   butter

tooth + brush = _____

1. _____

butter + bug = fly

2. _____

pan + cake = _____

3. _____

hand + bag = _____

4. _____

cup + board = _____

5. _____

lady + bug = _____

6. _____

horse + shoe = _____

7. _____

Compound word usage
© 1989 by Incentive Publications. Inc., Nashville. TN.

Write the correct word under each picture.
Put the two words together to make a new word.

 †  =

1. _____ _____ _____

 †  =

2. _____ _____ _____

 † ... =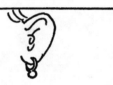

3. _____ _____ _____

 †  =

4. _____ _____ _____

 †  =

5. _____ _____ _____

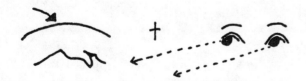 =

6. _____ _____ _____

 † ... =

7. _____ _____ _____

Compound word usage
© 1989 by Incentive Publications, Inc., Nashville, TN.

Compound words are made up of two smaller words.
Make as many compound words as you can by combining the words below.
Use a dictionary if you need help.
Write the words on another sheet of paper and then trade with a friend to see who
made the most words.

butter   store   man
class   shoe   news   cake   melon
black   mush   bed   horse
water   fly   milk
school   straw   lady   paper

MAYBE WE SHOULD GET TOGETHER SOMETIME!

sales   cup
berry   bug   room
pan   board   boy   cow
mail   sand   box   fall   rain
fire   house   horn   mate
back

Compound word usage
© 1989 by Incentive Publications, Inc., Nashville, TN.

*Answer Key

CLASSIFICATION TURN-ABOUT

Skills Purpose:
Classification

Unit Objective:
After completing this unit, students should be able to:
1. classify words and phrases.
2. classify ideas.
3. develop categories.
4. make functional use of words in a given category.

Preparation & Procedure:
1. Reproduce the activity sheets. Provide the students with pencils and dictionaries.
2. Verbally introduce the unit and present the activity sheets in the order necessary to meet students' needs.
3. Provide time for evaluation of each completed activity.

Optional Follow-up Activities:
1. Instead of having students name the words in each category, instruct the students to give clues and to ask friends to guess the correct words. Then the students may ask what the words have in common (page 71).
2. Have each student choose a partner and take turns naming items in each category. The winner is the person who names more items without repetition (page 72).
3. Let the students work in pairs or teams to see who can think of the most items in each category (page 73).
4. Ask each student to make up his or her own category cards. Make category suggestions such as the following:
   - items found in a classroom
   - items found in a kitchen
   - items found in a bedroom

Write the names of the pictures in the correct puzzle boxes.

Words to use:

coat	shirt	glove	blouse	belt
dress	hat	skirt	sweater	jacket
pants	socks	shoe	apron	

Across:

2.
4.
5.
7.
8.
11.
12.

Down:

1.
3.
6.
7.
8.
9.
10.

Classification
© 1989 by Incentive Publications, Inc., Nashville, TN.

*Answer Key

The words in each triangle have something in common.
They all belong to the same category.
Name the words to a friend and ask him or her to guess the category.

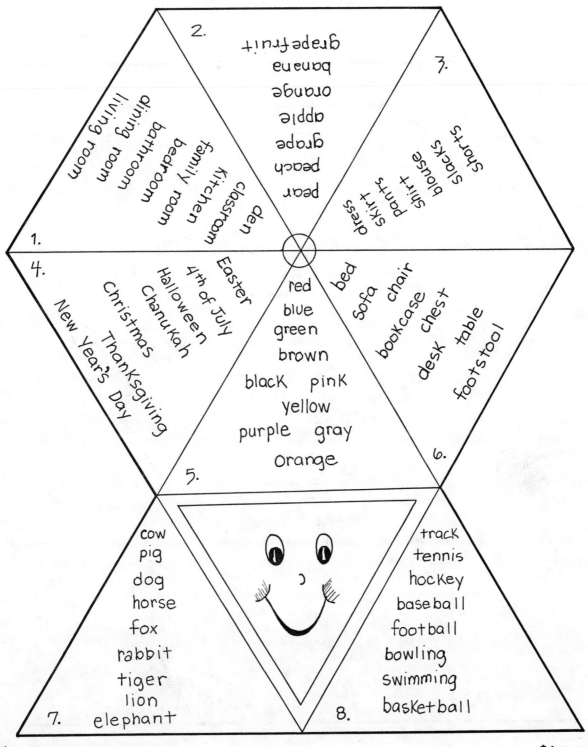

1.
dining room
living room
bathroom
bedroom
family room
kitchen
classroom
den

2.
pear
peach
grape
apple
orange
banana
grapefruit

3.
dress
skirt
pants
shirt
blouse
slacks
shorts

4.
Easter
4th of July
Halloween
Chanukah
Christmas
Thanksgiving
New Year's Day

5.
red
blue
green
brown
black   pink
yellow
purple   gray
orange

6.
bed
sofa   chair
bookcase
chest
desk   table
footstool

7.
cow
pig
dog
horse
fox
rabbit
tiger
lion
elephant

8.
track
tennis
hockey
baseball
football
bowling
swimming
basketball

Classification
© 1989 by Incentive Publications, Inc., Nashville, TN.

*Answer Key

❖ NAME _____

Cut out the category triangles.
Select a triangle and name items that belong to that category.

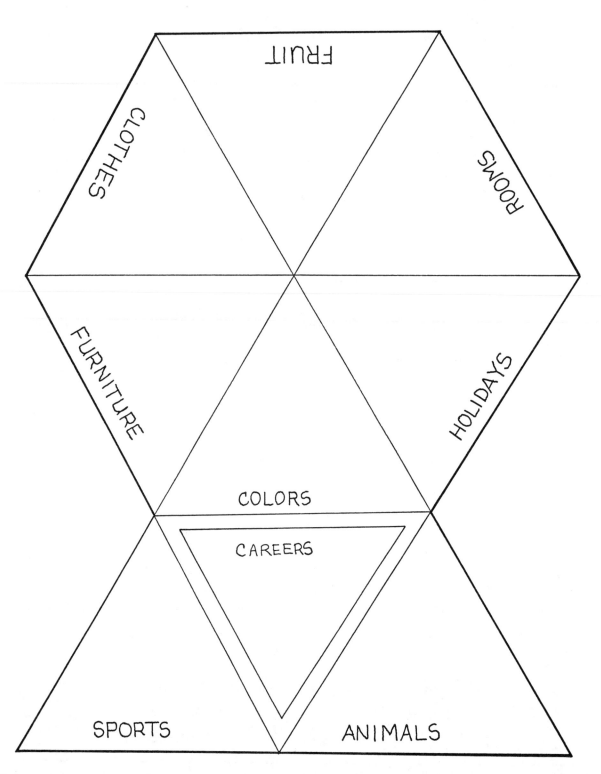

Select a triangle and fill it with words that belong in that category.

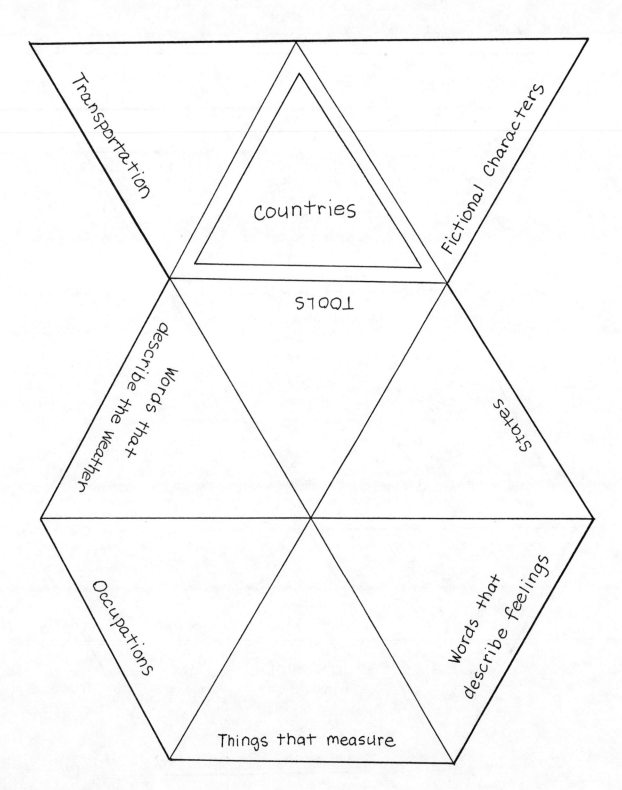

NAME

Choose a triangle and read the words to a friend.
Ask the friend to tell what the words have in common and to name the correct category.

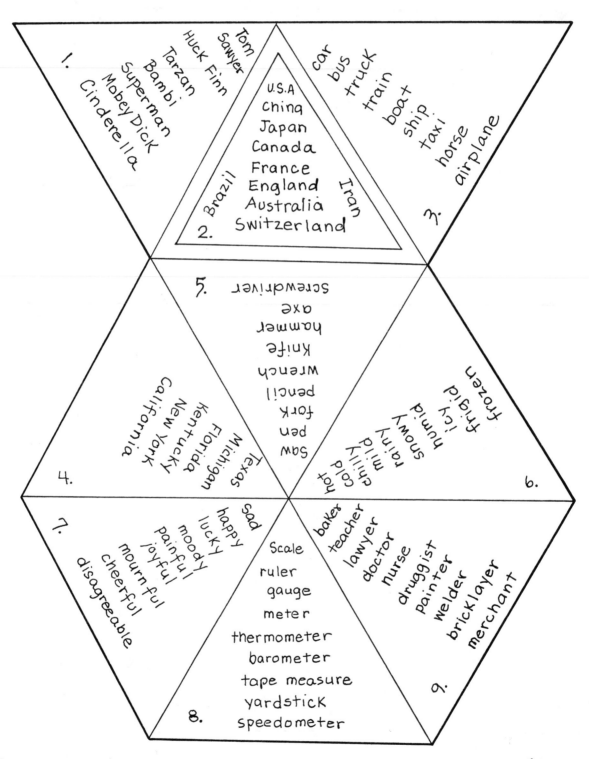

Classification
© 1989 by Incentive Publications, Inc., Nashville, TN.

*Answer Key

CONTEXT CONNECTIONS

Skills Purpose:
Using Context Clues

Unit Objectives:
After completing this unit, students should be able to:
1. use pictures as context clues.
2. complete sentences by using context clues.
3. use context clues to select appropriate words to complete sentences.

Preparation & Procedure:
1. Reproduce the activity sheets. Provide the students with reference books and pencils.
2. Verbally introduce and explain each activity.
3. Allow time for evaluation of each completed activity and give immediate feedback.
4. Make provision for sharing the completed activities.

Optional Follow-up Activity:
1. Have the students write five other sentences using words in the "word mixer" (page 78).

NAME _____

Circle the picture that completes each sentence.

1. A mailman delivers    .

2. A bird lays   .

3. She drank   .

4. A boy read a    .

5. He rode in a   .

6. A pilot flies an    .

Using context clues
© 1989 by Incentive Publications, Inc., Nashville, TN.

Circle the picture that completes each sentence.
Write the missing words in the blanks.

1. I answered the ringing _____ .

2. To get some fresh air he opened the _____ .

3. Before he read the letter he opened the _____ .

4. To carry water from the well he used a _____ .

5. It was raining so I took my _____ .

  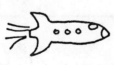

6. Astronauts fly to the _____ .

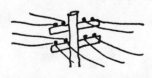

7. The hungry squirrel ran up the _____ .

Using context clues
© 1989 by Incentive Publications. Inc., Nashville, TN.

 NAME _____

Find the words in the "word mixer" to complete each sentence
Write the words in the blanks.

drove night with
ran
across ball hat to
plays window
truck cat eats moon
her drinks
down

1. Joe _____ his _____ to town.

2. Jan _____ with _____ dolls.

3. Tony _____ bread and _____ milk.

4. The _____ jumped on the _____ ledge.

5. Jim hit the _____ _____ his bat.

6. Cindy ran _____ the playground _____ the swing.

7. The _____ and stars shine at _____ .

8. Mr. Smith _____ to pick up his _____ that

   the wind had blown _____ the street.

Using context clues
© 1989 by Incentive Publications. Inc., Nashville. TN.

DOUBLE TALK

Skills Purpose:
Mental Imagery

Unit Objectives:
After completing this unit, students should be able to:
1. relate to figurative language.
2. associate figurative language and pictures.
3. make decisions related to the use of language references.

Preparation & Procedure:
1. Reproduce the activity sheets. Provide the students with pencils, crayons and construction paper.
2. Verbally introduce the activities.
3. Allow time for discussion and evaluation of each completed activity, and provide additional reinforcement as needed.
4. Assist the students in making decorative construction paper covers for their completed activity sheets. This makes a "fun" activity package to share with family or friends.

NAME _____

Draw a line from each descriptive phrase to the picture that illustrates it.

1.

2.

hungry as a bear

busy as a beaver

3.

working like a dog

free as the wind

4.

5.

fresh as a daisy

happy as a lark

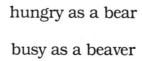

6.

sweet as sugar

pretty as a picture

8.

7.

fit as a fiddle

clear as glass

10.

9.

Mental Imagery
© 1989 by Incentive Publications, Inc., Nashville, TN.

Some words can be used in "funny ways."
Write the phrase that best describes each picture.

Phrases to use:
"beat the drum"
"two-faced"
"beside herself"
"starry-eyed"
"mad money"
"brainstorm"
"in the doghouse"
"for crying out loud"

1. _____

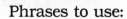

2. _____

3. _____

4. _____

5. _____

6. _____

7. _____

8. _____

 NAME _____

Read each set of sentences.
Circle the word that is the same in each set.
Draw a line from each sentence to the picture that describes it.

	If you're not careful, you'll slip! Sue wore a slip under her dress.	
	Quick, stamp on that bug! Sam put a stamp on the letter.	
	The task was to match the shapes. We need a match to start a fire.	
	The dress shop was having a big sale. She went to shop for groceries.	
	You must pick up everything you drop! Each drop told of her sadness.	
	Tim took time to watch his favorite show. Willy got a new watch.	
	Pam bought a pound of coffee. Pound the hammer to get attention!	
	Tom and Tim went outside to play ball. We enjoyed watching the play.	

Mental imagery
© 1989 by Incentive Publications, Inc., Nashville, TN.

HEAR YE! HEAR YE!

Skills Purpose:
Critical Listening

Unit Objectives:
After completing this unit, students should be able to:
1. listen to find answers to questions.
2. gain specific information from oral reading.
3. make inferences and draw conclusions.

Preparation & Procedure:
1. Reproduce the activity sheets.
2. To provide motivation and develop readiness for the unit, read aloud a section from a familiar book and ask the students to answer questions related to the story.
3. Explain the activities carefully and have the students work in pairs to complete the activities.
4. Encourage students to select stories or chapters from basal readers, library books or social studies texts to be used in a similar manner.

Optional Follow-up Activity:
1. Have each pair of students act out the story on page 85. Ask the students to show how they feel through their actions — happy, sad, angry or surprised.

Read this story to a friend.
Ask the friend to write his or her name at the top of this page and to answer the questions below.

> Joe and Sam made plans to play ball together.
>
> When Joe went to meet Sam, his friend was not there.
>
> He went to Sam's house and rang the doorbell.
>
> Sam's mother came to the door and said, "Hello, Joe.
>
> Sam has a bad cold and can't go outside."
>
> Joe was disappointed.
>
> He would have to wait for another day to play ball with his friend.

Questions:

1. Were Joe and Sam friends? _____

2. Did Sam's mother have a cold? _____

3. Was Joe able to come out and play? _____

4. Was Joe happy? _____

5. Who's who?
   Draw an X on the picture of Joe.
   Draw a circle around the picture of Sam.

Critical listening
© 1989 by Incentive Publications. Inc., Nashville. TN.

Read this story to a friend.
Ask the friend to write his or her name at the top of this page and to answer the
  questions at the end of the story.

> One day Tom was happily listening to his portable radio.
> His brother came over and grabbed the radio.
> Tom yelled angrily, "No! That's mine!
> I had it first!
> Give me that radio."
> The radio fell to the floor and broke.
> Both brothers were angry and sad.

Questions:

1. What was Tom listening to? _____

2. What did his brother do? _____

3. What happened to the radio? _____

4. Why were the boys angry? _____

5. Why were the boys sad? _____

6. Number the pictures in the order that best describes how Tom felt
   during the story.

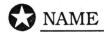

Read this story to a friend.

Ask the friend to write his or her name at the top of this page and to answer the questions at the end of the story.

It is Bob's birthday and he can't wait to find out what special present his parents have bought for him.

"What is my present?" Bob asked his mother over and over again.

"It's a surprise," she said. "I'll give you a hint, though. Your present has wheels and you can ride it."

Bob thought and thought. What could the surprise be? It has wheels. You can ride it. Maybe it is a big shiny car like his dad's.

"No," thought Bob, "I am too little to drive a car."

Maybe it is a fast, noisy motorcycle like his big brother's.

But Bob is too little to drive a motorcycle.

Maybe it is a boat. No, it couldn't be.

Boats don't have wheels.

He thought and thought. What has wheels and is just right for a boy his size to ride? Bob can't guess what the birthday present is. Can you?

Questions:

1. Why is the day special for Bob? _____

2. The surprise present isn't a car like Dad's. Why? _____

3. Why can't Bob's present be a motorcycle? _____

4. It can't be a boat. Why? _____

5. What do you think the present is? Why? _____

6. Circle the picture of the surprise present.

NON-SENSATIONAL

Skills Purpose:
Making Value Judgments

Unit Objectives:
After completing this unit, students should be able to:
1. relate sentences to pictures.
2. distinguish between sense and nonsense.
3. change nonsense sentences to sentences that make sense.

Preparation & Procedure:
1. Reproduce the activity sheets. Provide the students with pencils, art paper and pastel tempera paints.
2. Introduce the unit to enable the students to complete the activities as independently as possible.
3. Allow time for ongoing guidance and evaluation.
4. Ask each student to use art paper and tempera paints to make an attractive folder for the completed activity sheets.

Optional Follow-up Activity:
1. Ask each student to illustrate his or her favorite nonsense sentence from the story on page 93.

NAME _____

Read these nonsense sentences.
Circle the word in each sentence that
    is incorrect.

1. Don't full down the stairs.

2. The waiter put the foot on the table.

3. All that food made me fall.

4. I picked up a pan and started to write.

5. I mist you.

6. Tank you.

7. Little grills are made of sugar and spice.

8. Of horse you can do it.

9. I poured water in may cap.

10. The cupboard was bear.

11. I gave my hog a bone.

12. I live you.

13. Sting a song.

Making value judgments

Sandy wants a special shoe, but she can't remember the name of the shoe she
    wants.
All she knows is what she doesn't want!
Read these statements and put an X on each shoe that Sandy does *not* want.

Sandy says:

"I don't want a boot."

"I don't want a sandal."

"I don't want a ballet shoe."

"I don't want a shoe with words on it."

"I don't want an ice skate."

"I don't want a lady's high heel shoe."

"I don't want a moccasin."

"I don't want a shoe with a buckle."

"I don't want a shoe with dots on it."

"I don't want a football shoe."

Circle the shoe that is left to find out what Sandy wants to buy.

Making value judgments
© 1989 by Incentive Publications, Inc., Nashville, TN.

*Answer Key

Read these sentences to a friend.
Ask the friend to tell you what is wrong with each sentence.

1. I am bigger than a house and smaller than a breadbox.
2. I drank the sandwich and ate the milk.
3. The weather report predicted showers, so I went to the store to buy some soap.
4. Smell me a story.
5. I got out of the car and drove away.
6. I turned off the switch and the light came on.
7. I put my sandwich in the refrigerator and sat down to eat it.
8. I put on my gloves to keep my feet warm.
9. I had such a nice train ride across the ocean.
10. I called you on the telephone so I could see you.
11. I wanted to get a higher salary, so I took my ladder to work.
12. I went to the library because I was hungry.
13. I turned the heat on because I was hot.
14. Listen to the picture and look at the sound.
15. I put my boots on my head.

Read these nonsense sentences.
Rewrite the sentences so they make sense.

NONSENSE SENTENCE	SENSIBLE SENTENCE
1. Don't cry over spelled milk.	1.
2. I was tired sew I took a map.	2.
3. You deserve a brake today.	3.
4. If you're stick, go to bad.	4.
5. I tore the ham in my coat.	5.
6. I licked an ice scream comb.	6.
7. Pardon me, but your ship is showing.	7.
8. We need some light. Please burn on the lamb.	8.
9. If the shoe fats, where it.	9.
10. You made your bread, now lye in it.	10.
11. Mother went into the kitchen to fly the chicken.	11.
12. I lake to sale on the like.	12.

Making value judgments
© 1989 by Incentive Publications, Inc., Nashville, TN.

Willy often says the opposite of what he means to say.
Read the story to see how misplaced words get him into trouble.

This morning, Willy went to school and said, "Good *night*, Mrs. Jones. Here is an apple for you. I like you because you are a *bad* teacher — and you're *ugly* too!"

Mrs. Jones took the roll. When she called Willy's name, he raised his hand and said, "I'm *absent* today."

After lunch Mrs. Jones said, "Willy, you failed the test again."

Willy lowered his head and said, "I feel *happy* about that. I'll study *less* next time."

Rewrite the story using these words in place of the underlined words:

present   unhappy   more   morning
                 pretty   good

_____

_____

_____

_____

_____

_____

Read this story to a friend.
Ask the friend to stop you each time there is a nonsense sentence and to change the wording so that the story makes sense.

Silly
Farmer Jones

Farmer Jones put on his rain boots because it was such a sunny, dry day. He went to the barn to feed his children. The chickens said "quack" as he milked the family horse. The farmer then went into the playground to feed the pigs and to see if the cow had laid some eggs for his breakfast.

Farmer Jones went back to his house and his wife fixed him scrambled bacon and tossed eggs. He finished drinking his paper and read the coffee.

After his meal, Farmer Jones got into his bed and drove to town. He went to the barber shop to have his grass cut and to talk to his friend, the chair.

At sunrise the farmer went to sleep because he had put in a full day's work and because he was so wide awake.

Making value judgments
© 1989 by Incentive Publications, Inc., Nashville, TN.

Make up your own nonsense sentences.
Ask a friend to rewrite the sentences so they make sense.

1.	1.
2.	2.
3.	3.
4.	4.
5.	5.
6.	6.
7.	7.
8.	8.
9.	9.
10.	10.
11.	11.
12.	12.

Making value judgments
© 1989 by Incentive Publications. Inc.. Nashville. TN.

NEXT STEP

Skills Purpose:
Sequencing

Unit Objectives:
After completing this unit, students should be able to:
1. use picture clues to develop and tell a story with plot and sequence.
2. order and reorder picture clues to develop and tell a story in more than one way.
3. make a creative contribution to sequences of picture clues to be used in the development of an original story.

Preparation & Procedure:
1. Reproduce the activity sheets. Provide the students with paste, scissors and extra paper.
2. Verbally introduce the unit.
3. Arrange conference times for discussion and evaluation of each completed activity, and provide additional reinforcement as needed.
4. Make provision for sharing picture sequences in a group setting and for filing or displaying all of the completed activity sheets.

Draw a line through the maze to show the correct
sequence.
Tell a story to go with the pictures.

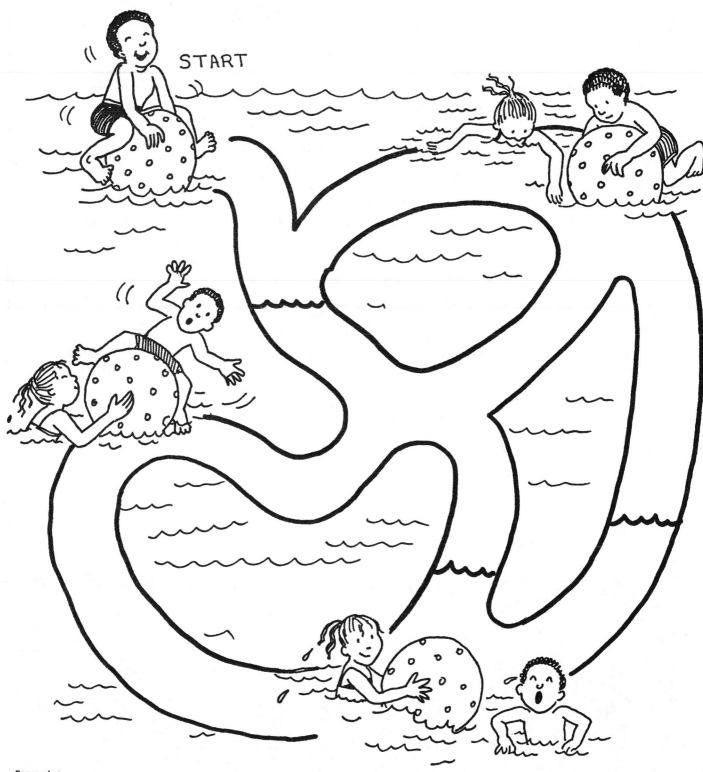

START

Sequencing
© 1989 by Incentive Publications, Inc., Nashville, TN.

*Answer Key

◆ NAME

1. Use these pictures to tell a story.
2. Number the pictures in the order the story is told.
3. Reorder the pictures, and tell the story in another way.

What happens next?

Sequencing
© 1989 by Incentive Publications, Inc., Nashville, TN.

1. Tell what happened in each picture sequence.
2. Tell what might happen next in each sequence.
3. Draw pictures to illustrate what you have described.

What happens next?

What happens next?

What happens next?

What happens next?

Sequencing
© 1989 by Incentive Publications, Inc., Nashville, TN.

PICT-O-GRAM

Skills Purpose:
Picture-Word Associations

Unit Objectives:
After completing this unit, students should be able to:
1. match words and pictures.
2. associate symbols with words.
3. use word and symbol associations to read a story.
4. use picture symbols to create an original story.

Preparation & Procedure:
1. Reproduce the activity sheets.
2. Discuss the pictures and symbols in as much detail as necessary to enable the students to complete the activities.
3. Let the students work in pairs to complete the activities and to "check" each other's completed work.
4. Make provision for filing or displaying the completed activity sheets.

Picture and Symbol List

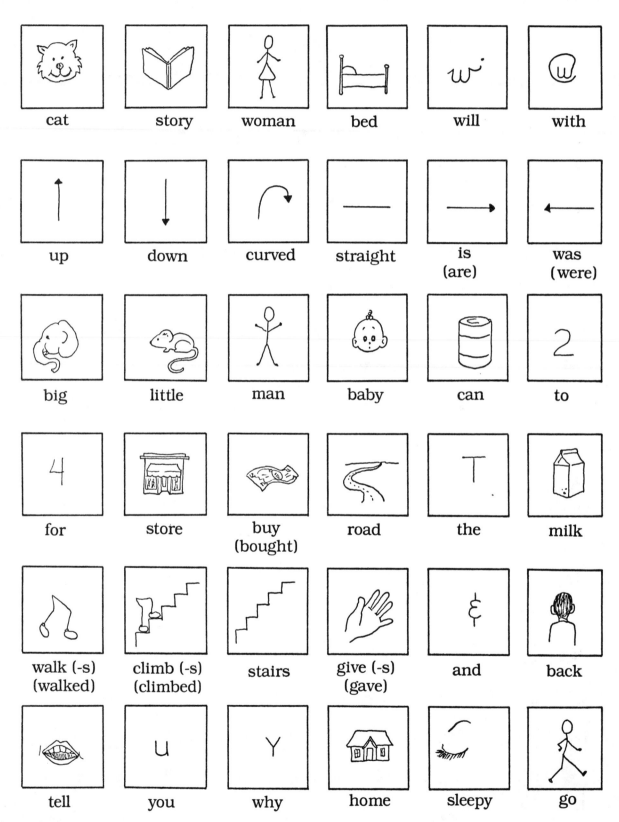

cat	story	woman	bed	will	with
up	down	curved	straight	is (are)	was (were)
big	little	man	baby	can	to
for	store	buy (bought)	road	the	milk
walk (-s) (walked)	climb (-s) (climbed)	stairs	give (-s) (gave)	and	back
tell	you	why	home	sleepy	go

Picture-word associations
© 1989 by Incentive Publications, Inc., Nashville, TN.

Use the picture and symbol list to match each word with the correct picture.

can

big

little

buy

climb

tell

give

back

walk

home

store

go

sleepy

man

woman

stairs

road

story

Use the picture and symbol list to match each word with the correct symbol.

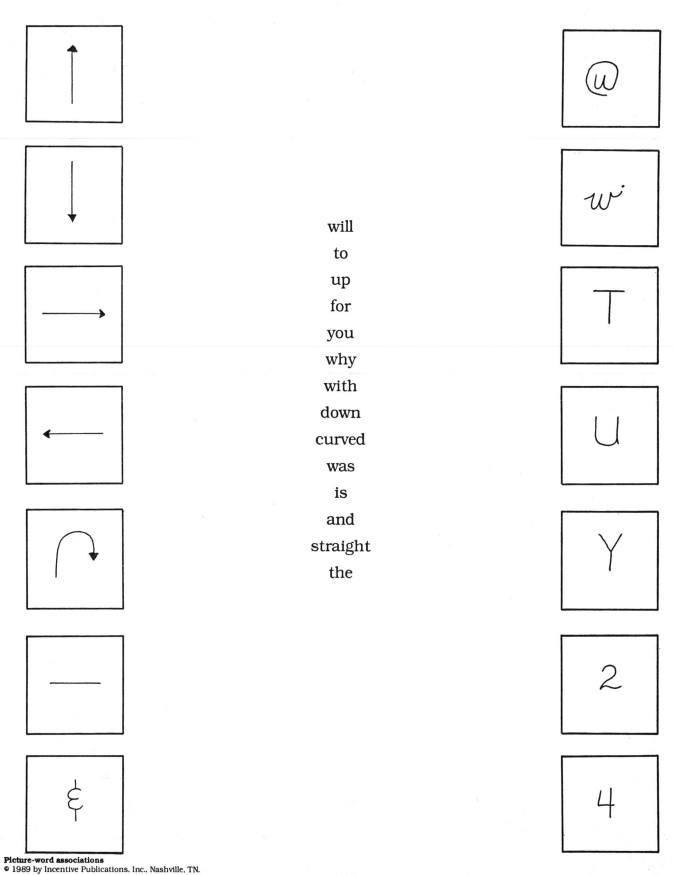

will

to

up

for

you

why

with

down

curved

was

is

and

straight

the

Use the picture and symbol list to read each story.
Write the correct word under each picture and symbol.

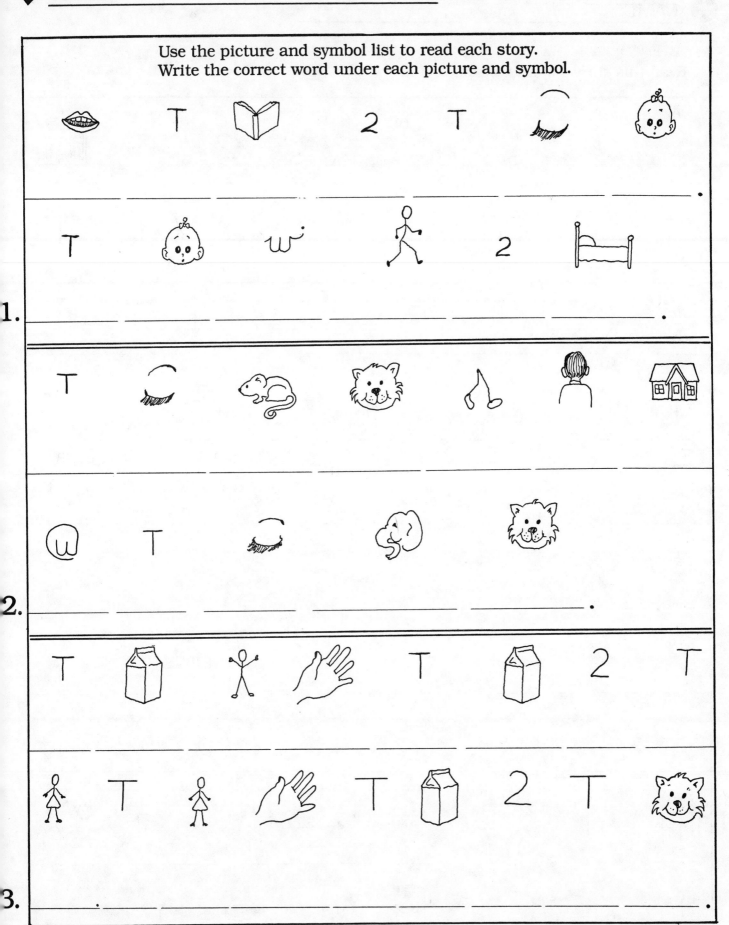

1. _____ .

2. _____ .

3. _____ .

Picture-word associations
© 1989 by Incentive Publications. Inc., Nashville, TN.

*Answer Key

Read this story aloud to a friend.

Picture-word associations
© 1989 by Incentive Publications, Inc., Nashville, TN.

*Answer Key

Make your own picture and symbol list.
Try to make your list as creative as possible.

Write your own pict-o-story.
Use pictures and symbols from your own picture and
    symbol list.
Ask a friend to read your story.

oink!!

QUESTION BOX

Skills Purpose:
Critical Reading

Unit Objectives:
After completing this unit, students should be able to:
1. use visual clues to find answers to questions.
2. use context clues to find answers to questions.
3. note details in order to gain information.
4. find answers to questions by drawing inferences from written material.

Preparation & Procedure:
1. Reproduce the activity sheets and provide the students with pencils and paper. Secure a loose leaf notebook and title it "Question Box Stories."
2. Verbally introduce the unit and discuss sample items to enable the students to complete the activities as independently as possible.
3. Allow time for ongoing guidance and evaluation.
4. Make provision for filing or displaying the completed activity sheets. Add creative stories to the "Question Box Stories" collection.

Optional Follow-up Activities:
1. Have each student write about what will happen next in the story on page 108.
2. Instruct the students to look up any unfamiliar words found in the reports on page 112.

Read the story to find answers to these questions.

1. What happened at 9:00 in the morning? _____

_____

2. What happened at 9:00 at night? _____

_____

3. Where did the boy put his toys? _____

_____

4. How many hours did he work? _____

Critical reading _____
© 1989 by Incentive Publications, Inc., Nashville, TN.

Read the story to find answers to these questions.

1. Why did the cat leave home? _____

_____

2. List three reasons why he came back home.

_____

_____

_____

Title: _____

Read the story to find answers to these questions.

1. Why did Hattie want to wear a hat to school? _____

2. Why did her mother want her to take an umbrella? _____

3. How did the other students feel about her hat? _____

4. What happened on the way home from school? _____

5. Describe how Hattie felt after she got home. _____

6. Give the story a title.

Critical reading
© 1989 by Incentive Publications, Inc., Nashville, TN.

Want To Play?

Read the story to find answers to these questions.

1   What are four reasons why Joey had no friends?

   _____

   _____

   _____

2. If you were Joey, what would you do to make friends? _____

   _____

3. What is another good title for this story? _____

   _____

Critical reading
© 1989 by Incentive Publications, Inc., Nashville, TN.

The first men to successfully fly an airplane were Wilbur and Orville Wright. This first flight was at Kitty Hawk, North Carolina on December 17, 1903.

Charles Lindberg was the first aviator to cross the Atlantic Ocean. This flight was on May 21, 1927.

On July 20, 1969, Neil Armstrong was flung into orbit around the moon by a large rocket. He landed on the moon with the aid of small rockets and left his footprint on another world.

The first operational jet airplanes were introduced by the German Air Force in 1945. DeHavilland Comet Airliners, flying for a British airline, introduced the jet age to civilians in the 1950s.

American and Russian astronauts demonstrated the growth from flight in air to flight in space by orbiting the earth together in July of 1975.

List the six important flight events and their dates given in the report above.

1. _____

2. _____

3. _____

4. _____

5. _____

6. _____

Critical reading
© 1989 by Incentive Publications, Inc., Nashville, TN.

*Answer Key

READER'S CHOICE

Skills Purpose:
Analogies

Unit Objectives:
After completing this unit, students should be able to:
1. associate related concepts.
2. infer relationships in order to complete thoughts.
3. draw conclusions.

Preparation & Procedure:
1. Reproduce the activity sheets and provide the students with colored chalk.
2. Verbally introduce the unit.
3. Instruct each student to select a partner to work with and to follow the activity directions.
4. Arrange time for discussion and ongoing evaluation of the activities, and provide individual guidance and reinforcement as needed.
5. Make provision for sharing ideas in a group setting and for filing the completed activity sheets.

Optional Follow-up Activity:
1. Ask the students to think of other items which the color words on page 116 might be used to describe.

Circle the picture that completes each analogy.

1. Fingers are to _____ as toes are to _____

2. Round is to _____ as square is to _____

3. Hammer is to _____ as bat is to _____

4. Air is to _____ as water is to _____

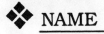

Circle the correct word to complete each analogy.

1. Calf is to ___ as kitten / puppy is to ___

2. Day is to ___ as star / night is to ___

3. Smell is to ___ as nose / noise is to ___

4. Bracelet is to ___ as glove / ring is to ___

5. Ink is to ___ as lead / eraser is to ___

6. Temperature is to ___ as size / time is to ___

Analogies
© 1989 by Incentive Publications. Inc., Nashville, TN.

Find the color words to complete these phrases, and write the correct words in the
puzzle boxes.

Across

2. _____ as grass
3. _____ as dirt
7. _____ is for cotton candy
8. _____ hot
9. _____ grape juice

Down

1. sunshine _____
3. _____ as night
4. _____ as a pumpkin
5. _____ as snow
6. _____ skies

Color Words

red
blue
orange
black
white
green
brown
pink
yellow
purple

Analogies
© 1989 by Incentive Publications, Inc., Nashville, TN.

*Answer Key

Write the missing word in the blank to make each statement true.

Words to use: fall   south   hear
                 go   ear   window
                 happy   dark

1.
Talking is to the mouth

as

hearing is to the _____ .

2.
Red is to stop

as

green is to _____ .

3.
East is to west

as

north is to _____ .

4.
A frown is to sad

as

a smile is to _____ .

5.
A rug is to a floor

as

a curtain is to a _____ .

6.
White is to black

as

light is to _____ .

7.
A book is to read

as

a record is to _____ .

8.
Summer is to winter

as

spring is to _____ .

Write the missing word in the blank to make each statement true.

1.
A dictionary is to words

as

an _____ is to maps.

2.
Low is to a valley

as

high is to a _____ .

3.
Tracks are to a train

as

_____ are to a car.

4.
Electricity is to a television

as

_____ is to a car.

5.
North America is to Canada

as

_____

is to Brazil.

6.
Washington, D.C. is to the
United States of America

as

_____ is to Mexico.

7.
Leaving is to departing

as

_____ is to arriving.

8.
Boy is to "son"

as

_____ is to "daughter."

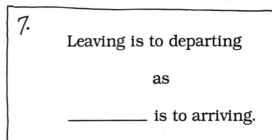

Analogies
© 1989 by Incentive Publications, Inc., Nashville, TN.

*Answer Key

RIDDLE ROUNDUP

Skills Purpose:
Making Inferences

Unit Objectives:
After completing this unit, students should be able to:
1. read to reach conclusions.
2. set purposes to guide listening and thinking.
3. use context clues to make independent judgments.

Preparation & Procedure:
1. Reproduce the activity sheets and provide the students with pencils, dictionaries and two or three riddle books.
2. Lead a discussion of riddles and share the riddle books as motivation for the activities. Discuss the unit and ask each student to work with a friend to complete the activities. Encourage student independence by suggesting the use of the dictionary if help is needed to correctly spell the answers to the riddles.
3. Make provision for filing or displaying the completed activity sheets.
4. Ask the students to develop additional "Riddle Roundup" work sheets to trade with classmates, to find a riddle book in the library to add to the class collection, or to select a favorite riddle to illustrate.

Read each set of clues to a friend.
Ask the friend to guess who you are.

1. I wear a badge.
    I wear a uniform.
    I direct traffic.
    Safety is my job.
    My car has a siren and a flashing
        light.

    I am a _____ .

    Which hat would I wear?

2. I slide down poles.
    I ride in a truck.
    I work with water, a hose, and
        ladders.
    I put out fires.

    I am a _____ .

    What is _not_ a tool of my trade?

3. I wear white.
    I carry a black bag.
    Health is my business.
    I work in a hospital.
    A nurse is my helper.

    I am a _____ .

    What tool is a part of my trade?

4. I work in an office.
    I work with brushes.
    I work with drills.
    When you come to see me, you
        open your mouth.
    Teeth are my business.

    I am a _____ .

    Which part of your body do I help?

Making inferences
© 1989 by Incentive Publications, Inc., Nashville, TN.

Read each set of clues to a friend.
Ask the friend to tell what season you are describing.

1. Birds fly north.
    Days are longer and warmer.
    The wind blows and kites fly.
    Showers bring flowers.

    Colors change from gray to green.
    The goundhog looks for his
        shadow as a sign of

    _____ .

2. Days are short and nights are
        long.
    Warm clothes must be worn.
    Rain turns to ice and snow.
    I am best known for my color of
        white.

    Snowmen, sleds and a new year
        are signs of

    _____ .

3. Days are long and the
        temperature rises.
    It is a time for outdoor play.

    Swimming is a favorite sport.
    Heavy clothes are not for me!
    Picnics, camping and carefree
        days are signs of

    _____ .

4. Days grow shorter and sweaters
        are worn.
    Leaves change color and start to
        fall.
    When I begin, so does school.

    Animals prepare for winter.
    Ghosts, goblins, turkeys and
        feasts are signs of

    _____ .

Illustrate your favorite season.

Making Inferences
© 1989 by Incentive Publications, Inc., Nashville, TN.

 _____

Solve these riddles.

1. I have legs and a back but cannot walk. _____

2. People see through my panes. _____

3. You may know me by my bark but I make no sound. _____

4. People walk all over me but I don't mind. _____

5. I can fly but I need a pole. _____

6. I have a ring but no fingers. _____

7. I tell time but cannot speak. _____

8. The more I get sharpened, the shorter I become.

   _____

9. I look like you until you go away.

   _____

10. I travel many places but always go in circles.

    _____

11. I am always in a place where two things meet, but no

    one ever says "hello." _____ .

Word Clues:		
wheel	window	pencil
chair	mirror	telephone
tree	clock	floor
corner	flag	

Making Inferences
© 1989 by Incentive Publications, Inc., Nashville, TN.

STATE YOUR POSITION

Skills Purpose:
Using Position Words

Unit Objectives:
After completing this unit, students should be able to:
1. use position words in a problem-solving setting.
2. follow directions featuring position words.
3. use position words to express original thoughts.

Preparation & Procedure:
1. Reproduce the activity sheets. Provide the students with pencils and red felt-tip markers.
2. Verbally introduce the unit and play a game using position words to develop readiness for the activities.
3. Let the students work in pairs to complete the activities and to check each other's work.
4. Make provision for filing or displaying the completed activities.

Follow these directions to find your way through the maze.

1. Find the boy sitting beside the water.
2. Find the girl who is going into the water.
3. Next, go to the girl who is in the water.
4. Move to the girl who is in the water and running after the ball.
5. Find the girl who is on top of the water.
6. Draw a red circle around the other person who is out of the water.

Using position words
© 1989 by Incentive Publications, Inc., Nashville, TN.

*Answer Key

Cut out the hat and the newspaper below.
Cut along the dotted lines to make four slots.
Give this activity to a friend and ask the friend to follow these
    directions as you read them aloud.

1. Put the hat on the man's head.
2. Put the newspaper over his stomach.
3. Put the hat on top of the newspaper.
4. Now, put the hat beside the newspaper.
5. Put the hat under the newspaper.

Ask your friend to use position words such as *on, over, under,* and
    beside to tell where the man, the hat, and the newspaper are in
    relation to the other items.

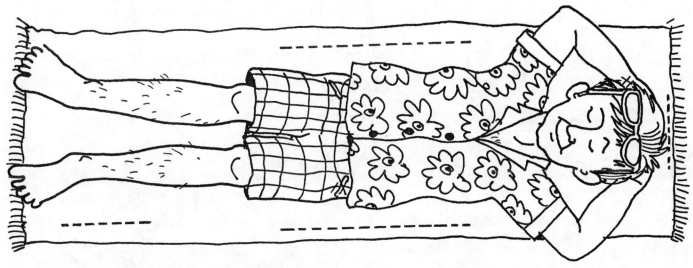

Using position words
© 1989 by Incentive Publications, Inc., Nashville, TN.

Give a copy of this activity sheet to a friend.
Ask the friend to find each picture as you tell about it.
Be sure to use position words to help make your descriptions easier to follow.

Using position words
© 1989 by Incentive Publications, Inc., Nashville, TN.

WORK STUDY SKILLS

ALPHABET ANNIE

Skills Purpose:
Alphabetizing

Unit Objectives:
After completing this unit, students should be able to:
1. arrange letters in alphabetical order.
2. order words alphabetically.
3. use alphabetical order to arrange words in sentences.

Preparation & Procedure:
1. Reproduce the activity sheets. Provide the students with pencils, crayons, glue, and poster board.
2. Verbally introduce the unit in a "fun" manner.
3. Allow time for guidance and continuing evaluation.
4. Make provision for the students to glue their completed activity sheets on poster board to be displayed in the classroom.

Optional Follow-up Activity:
1. Ask the students to make up their own "alphabetical" sentences.

Alphabet Annie is having a terrible time trying to learn to
    use her dictionary.
One of her problems is that she never has learned to put
    words in alphabetical order.
Try to complete all of the activities in this unit
    so that you will not find yourself in the same
    predicament.
Begin by arranging the letters in Alphabet
    Annie's soup bowl in alphabetical order.

A ___ ___ ___ ___ ___ ___ ___ ___

___ ___ ___ ___ ___ ___ ___ ___

___ ___ ___ ___ ___ ___ ___ Z ___

Alphabetizing
© 1989 by Incentive Publications, Inc., Nashville, TN.

Find these words in the puzzle and circle them.

a	my
an	net
at	news
ate	no
is	owe
mat	say
me	so
men	yes

a n o i

n e w s

a t e a

m e m y

e s a e

n o t s

Alphabetizing
© 1989 by Incentive Publications, Inc., Nashville, TN.

*Answer Key

Alphabetize the words in each row.
Write the words in alphabetical order to make a sentence.
Capitalize and punctuate each sentence correctly.

1.   dogs   angry   growl

_____

2.   high   birds   fly

_____

3.   elephants   peanuts   munch

_____

4.   a   the   cow   fell   careless   in   water

_____

Alphabetizing
© 1989 by Incentive Publications, Inc., Nashville, TN.

NAME _____

Alphabetize the words in each row.
Write the words in alphabetical order to make a sentence.
Capitalize and punctuate each sentence correctly.

1. good   very   swinger   a   well   swings

   _____

2.   me   smile   cartoons   make

   _____

3. reading   sad   Tom   after   weeps   stories

   _____

4.   begged   Al   wash   Bob   weekly   to

   _____

Alphabetizing
© 1989 by Incentive Publications, Inc., Nashville, TN.

NAME _____

Alphabetize the words in each row.
Write the words in alphabetical order to make a sentence.
Draw a line from each sentence to the picture that best describes it.

1.   canoes   can   crocodiles   crazy   carry

_____

2.   watching   win   wonderful   was   Willy

_____

3. her fed Dora kangaroo olives daffy oily jumping

_____

4.   drawings   Debbie   drab   dear   does

_____

5.   happy has humor Harry horrible handsome

_____

6.   sick saved sailors sinking sailing survivors seven

_____

Alphabetizing
© 1989 by Incentive Publications, Inc., Nashville, TN.

134

COMPUTER MATCH

Skills Purpose:
Organizing Information

Unit Objectives:
After completing this unit, students should be able to:
1. gather specific information.
2. record information gained.
3. compute data in a meaningful sense.

Preparation & Procedure:
1. Reproduce the activity sheets. Provide the students with pencils and paper.
2. Verbally introduce the unit and provide motivation for its completion by leading a discussion on how gathering and categorizing information can make daily life easier and more interesting.
3. Allow students to work together to complete the activities.
4. Make provision for ongoing evaluation and give as much immediate feedback as possible.
5. Ask the students to take home their completed activities to share with family members or friends.

NAME _____

Interview friends with this "computer questionnaire."
Keep a record of the answers and match the people who have the most in common.

Activity Match-Up Computer Questionnaire

Procedure:
1. List the names of the people interviewed.
2. Ask each person if he or she likes to do each activity listed. (For example: "Do you like to go to the movies?")
3. If the answer is "yes," put a check in the correct box.

Names	watch movies	dance	listen to music	play baseball	swim	read	watch T.V.	write	draw	go to school	sing
1.											
2.											
3.											
4.											
5.											
6.											

Organizing information
© 1989 by Incentive Publications, Inc., Nashville, TN.

❖ **NAME** _____

Answer these questions about yourself:

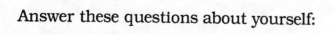

1. What is the color of your eyes? _____

2. What is the color of your hair? _____

3. What is the month of your birthday? _____

4. Where were you born? _____

5. What is the first letter of your first name? _____

6. What is your favorite food? _____

7. What is your least favorite food? _____

8. What is your favorite color? _____

9. What is your favorite song? _____

10. What is your favorite school subject? _____

11. What is your favorite sport? _____

12. What is your favorite television show? _____

_____

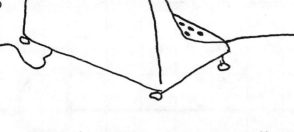

Write the answers to your questions in the numbered spaces on the Computer Sheet for Compatible Companions (page 138).

Example: If your answer to #1 is brown, write "brown" in space #1.

THESE ARE MY ANSWERS.
Which friend has the most in common with me?
NAMES:
Amy

Interview your friends, asking them the same questions you answered about yourself. If a friend's answer matches yours, put a check in the correct box beside his or her name.

Count the checks to see which friend has the most in common with you.

COMPUTER SHEET
FOR
COMPATIBLE COMPANIONS

THESE ARE MY ANSWERS →

Which friend has the
most in common with
me?

NAMES:

	1.	2.	3.	4.	5.	6.	7.	8.	9.	10.	11.	12.

Draw a portrait of your most compatible companion.

Write your own interview questions in the blanks below.
Suggested topics for questions are sports, television, clothes, music, food, hobbies, home responsibilities, future plans, etc.
Record the interview questions and the data you receive on the interview computer form below.

JUST THE FACTS, MA'AM!

1. _____
2. _____
3. _____
4. _____
5. _____
6. _____
7. _____

Interview Computer Form

Names

Questions

Names	1.	2.	3.	4.	5.	6.	7.

Organizing information
© 1989 by Incentive Publications, Inc., Nashville, TN.

CONCRETE CHARLIE'S CORRECTION CORNER

Skills Purpose:

Punctuation and Word Usage

Unit Objectives:

After completing this unit, students should be able to:
1. use punctuation marks correctly.
2. use contractions and abbreviations.
3. find and correct mistakes in written materials.

Preparation & Procedure:
1. Make a large paper cutout of "Concrete Charlie" and place it in the center of a bulletin board. Around Charlie's head place question marks, periods, etc. cut from construction paper. Provide the students with activity sheets, reference books, and pencils.
2. Explain each of the activities and encourage the students to use the reference books for help if necessary.
3. Provide time for evaluation of each completed activity and give immediate feedback.
4. Ask each student to select one completed activity sheet that he or she feels is representative of his or her best work and add it to the bulletin board display.

Charlie spells everything, even punctuation marks.
Read this letter that he wrote to Mary.
Rewrite the letter correctly at the bottom of the page.

Wed period comma Sept period eight

Dear Mary comma new paragraph I apostrophe m going to have a party on Friday comma September ten at four o apostrophe clock period Will you be able to come question mark new paragraph I talked to Jim and he said comma quotation marks I would love to come to the party exclamation point quotation marks new paragraph I think that a lot of people will be there period I hope that you will be there too exclamation point new paragraph I apostrophe ll be anxious to hear your reply period

Sincerely comma

Charlie

Rewrite this story.
To save time and space, use these abbreviations and contractions in place of the underlined words.

Mrs.	eve.	.Mass.	Blvd.
Mr.	didn't	Calif.	morn.
Jr.	sta.	St.	Feb.
Dr.	couldn't	Ave.	wouldn't
apt.	Miss.	Jan.	Wed.
bldg.	25	doz.	Mon.

Charlie Jones, Junior had a doctor's appointment on Monday, January twenty-fifth. The doctor's office was in an office building on the corner of Mississippi Street and California Drive.

Charlie's neighbor, Mister Smith, offered to drive him in his car from their apartment building on Massachusetts Boulevard to the doctor's office. Unfortunately, Mister Smith's car did not start.

Charlie went to the bus station, but the bus did not stop. He called a dozen taxis, but they could not come.

It was so late that he called the doctor's office to talk to the nurse, Mistress Lee. He told her he would not be able to come to the office that morning for his appointment and asked if he could make another one for the first Wednesday evening in February.

_____

_____

_____

_____

_____

_____

_____

Find and circle 18 errors Charlie made in this letter.
Correct the mistakes and rewrite the letter below.

15 Away place
birmingham : Michigan
May 10, 19

Sound Record Company
main Stree
Detroit , Michigan

Dear sir

I'd like to apply for the job you advertised in the school newspaper.

i am a good worker? I can work in the afternoon and all day on saturday.

I want to learn more about the job. please right to me at the above Address.

"Thank you,"   Sincerely ...
                              Charlie

_____
_____
_____
_____
_____
_____
_____
_____
_____
_____

Punctuation & word usage
© 1989 by Incentive Publications, Inc., Nashville, TN.

*Answer Key

DIRECTION DETECTION

Skills Purpose:
Following Directions

Unit Objectives:
After completing this unit, students should be able to:
1. follow simple written directions.
2. follow directions dependent on picture interpretation.
3. find answers to puzzles by following directions.

Preparation & Procedure:
1. Reproduce the activity sheets. Provide the students with black and blue felt-tip markers; blue, red, yellow, green, black, brown, pink, and orange colored chalk; scissors and glue. Create an attractive display area and label it "Hidden Numbers."
2. Discuss the importance of learning to follow directions (tell a funny story about someone who does not know how to follow directions). Introduce the activities in detail to enable the students to work as independently as possible.
3. Instruct the students to find and color the hidden numbers as directed on page 146, to cut out the finished design, and to add their designs to the bulletin board display.
4. Provide ongoing guidance and evaluation to encourage completion of the other activities.

Find and color the hidden numbers.

Color the 1 blue.

Color the 2 red.

Color the 3 yellow.

Color the 4 green.

Color the 5 black.

Color the 6 red.

Color the 7 brown.

Color the 8 pink.

Color the 9 orange.

Following directions
© 1989 by Incentive Publications, Inc., Nashville, TN.

1. Color the dress of the girl wearing a big hat red.
2. Color the book the short girl is carrying blue.
3. Color the tall boy's sweater red.
4. Color the short boy's shirt yellow.
5. Color the tall girl's hat red and blue.
6. Color the short boy's hat green and yellow.

Following directions

The pirates their treasure did take
to a hiding place by the lake.
These directions they left to help you
search for the clue.

1. Cross out first circle.
2. Circle the largest circle.
3. Put an X on the smallest square.
4. Circle the middle square.
5. Underline the last triangle.
6. Circle the second triangle.
7. Color the third oval.
8. Circle the next to last oval.
   Write the letter of each circled shape
   in the blanks.

If you followed the directions correctly, you found the hiding place to be a

_____ .

Following directions
© 1989 by Incentive Publications, Inc., Nashville, TN.

Follow the directions given below to reach your "mystery" destination.

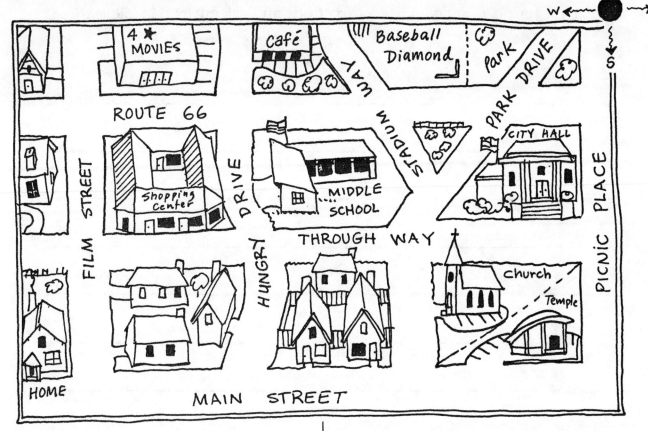

Mystery Car Ride #1

1. Start at **home**.

2. Drive straight on Main Street.

3. Drive to Hungry Drive and turn left.

4. Drive to Through Way and turn right.

5. Drive to Picnic Place and turn right.

6. Drive to Main Street and turn right.

7. Drive to Film Street and turn right.

8. Drive straight on Film Street to your destination.

You are at the _____ .
What will you do there?

Mystery Car Ride #2

1. Start at **home**.

2. Drive north on Film Street to Route 66.

3. Drive east on Route 66.

4. Drive south on Hungry Drive.

5. Drive east on Through Way.

6. Drive northeast on Park Drive.

7. Drive northwest on Stadium Way.

8. Drive west on Route 66.

9. Drive north on Hungry Drive to your destination.

You are at the _____ .
What will you do there?

★ NAME ______________________________

Make up your own set of mystery directions and ask a friend to follow them.

____

____

____

____

____

____

____

____

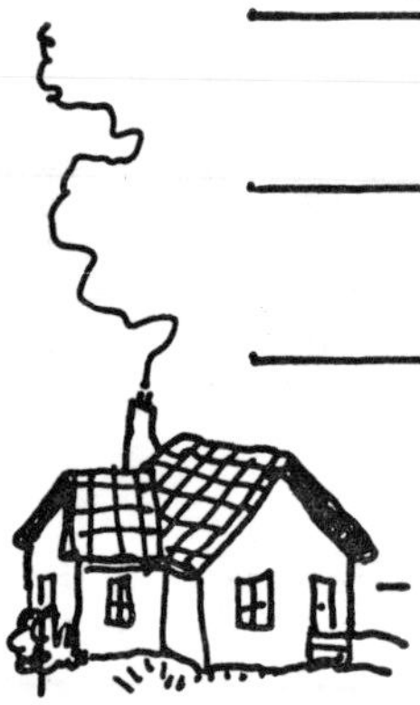

Draw a picture to make the directions more interesting and to give clues for solving the mystery.

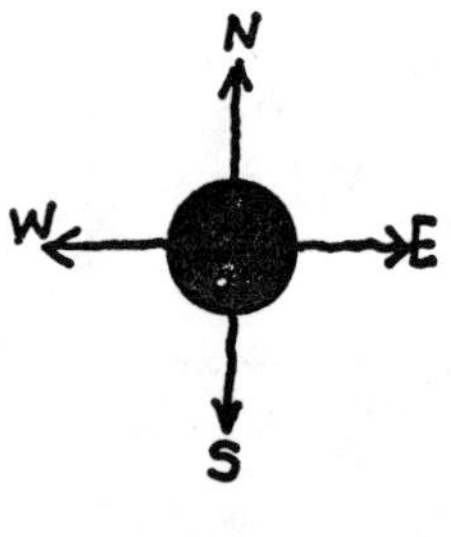

IF TRUE, DO

Skills Purpose:
Decision Making

Unit Objectives:
After completing this unit, students should be able to:
1. follow directions on the basis of decision making.
2. use written clues to arrive at a logical conclusion.
3. use creative resources to develop a puzzle.

Preparation & Procedure:
1. Reproduce the activity sheets. Provide the students with pencils, crayons, glue, scissors, and tagboard.
2. Verbally introduce the unit and discuss each puzzle in enough detail to allow the students to work independently.
3. Arrange to give ongoing guidance as the activity sheets are being completed.
4. Make provision for the students to cut out each completed puzzle and to glue it to a tagboard backing to form a "set" of puzzle cards that can be shared with friends or family.

To solve the puzzle and find the hidden word, read the sentences below.
If the statement is *true*, color the numbered puzzle spaces as directed.

					7
5	2	7	6	4	2
	9				5
9	1	5	3	9	8
	3 6				
7	8	4	2	4	1

1. If you see with your eyes, color the #1 spaces.

2. If you talk with your ears, color the #2 spaces.

3. If you walk on your lips, color the #3 spaces.

4. If you wiggle your toes, color the #4 spaces.

5. If you touch with your fingers, color the #5 spaces.

6. If you chew with your hands, color the #6 spaces.

7. If you smell with your nose, color the #7 spaces.

8. If your mouth is above your nose, color the #8 spaces.

9. If you bend at the waist, color the #9 spaces.

Decision making
© 1989 by Incentive Publications. Inc., Nashville, TN.

*Answer Key

To solve the puzzle and find the hidden word, read the sentences below.
If the statement is *true*, color the numbered puzzle spaces as directed.

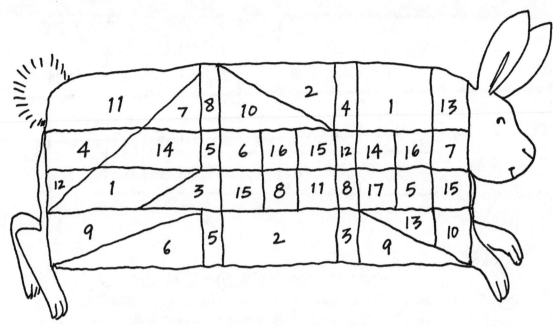

1. If cows give milk, color the #1 spaces.
2. If whales swim, color the #2 spaces.
3. If birds have scales, color the #3 spaces.
4. If roosters lay eggs, color the #4 spaces.
5. If lions have stripes, color the #5 spaces.
6. If camels have humps, color the #6 spaces.
7. If pigs "oink," color the #7 spaces.
8. If snakes are mammals, color the #8 spaces.
9. If squirrels eat nuts, color the #9 spaces.
10. If elephants have trunks, color the #10 spaces.
11. If a zebra has stripes, color the #11 spaces.
12. If chickens "quack," color the #12 spaces.
13. If spiders spin webs, color the #13 spaces.
14. If cats have fur, color the #14 spaces.
15. If an ant is an insect, color the #15 spaces.
16. If worms have feet, color the #16 spaces.
17. If eagles have feathers, color the #17 spaces.

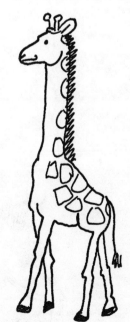

*Answer Key

To solve the puzzle and find the hidden word, read the sentences below.
If the statement is *true*, color the numbered puzzle spaces as directed.

2	1	5	15	8	13	11	14	1	3	9	4
20	17	3	4	13	2	6	3	16	20	17	2
2	18	6	16	12	9	22	1	8	5	16	10
21	9	5	23	22	21		23	14	7	15
3	7	13	21	16	6	19	13	11	1

1. If grass is green, color the #1 spaces.
2. If colors can be heard, color the #2 spaces.
3. If nouns are action words, color the #3 spaces.
4. If cars have wheels, color the #4 spaces.
5. If fish live in the air, color the #5 spaces.
6. If houses have rooms, color the #6 spaces.
7. If ice melts, color the #7 spaces.
8. If a bicycle has three wheels, color the #8 spaces.
9. If a tricycle has three wheels, color the #9 spaces.
10. If the letter "U" is a vowel, color the #10 spaces.
11. If a guitar is an instrument, color the #11 spaces.
12. If a baseball is a plant, color the #12 spaces.
13. If fire is cold, color the #13 spaces.
14. If hair grows, color the #14 spaces.
15. If scissors cut, color the #15 spaces.
16. If machines are alive, color the #16 spaces.
17. If the earth is a planet, color the #17 spaces.
18. If the sun is a star, color the #18 spaces.
19. If cities have streets, color the #19 spaces.
20. If rocks are food, color the #20 spaces.
21. If long means the same as short, color the #21 spaces.
22. If a library has books, color the #22 spaces.
23. If telephones answer, color the #23 spaces.

Decision making
© 1989 by Incentive Publications, Inc., Nashville, TN.

*Answer Key

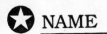

To solve the puzzle and find the hidden country, read the sentences below. If the statement is *true*, color the numbered puzzle spaces as directed.

2	9	12 2	5	13	10 3	6	5 2 15 1	9
15 4	11	15 8	14	10	11 13	9	1 12 6 9 4	6
12	1	2 12	6	5	10	14	15 2	14
8	4	15 9	13	3	5 8 7	5 12 7
15	2	8 11	3	10	1 4 11	14 15

1. If Mississippi is an ocean, color the #1 spaces blue.
2. If Tennessee is a state, color the #2 spaces red.
3. If Hawaii is a state, color the #3 spaces blue.
4. If Mexico is a country, color the #4 spaces red.
5. If Michigan is a country, color the #5 spaces red.
6. If Florida is a river, color the #6 spaces blue.
7. If Kentucky is in South America, color the #7 spaces red.
8. If Canada is a country, color the #8 spaces red.
9. If Washington, D.C. is the capital of Canada, color the #9 spaces blue.
10. If Washington is a state, color the #10 spaces blue.
11. If Ohio is an island, color the #11 spaces blue.
12. If New York is a city, color the #12 spaces red.
13. If California borders an ocean, color the #13 spaces blue.
14. If England is a continent, color the #14 spaces red.
15. If Australia is an island, color the #15 spaces red.

Decision making
© 1989 by Incentive Publications, Inc., Nashville, TN.

*Answer Key

 NAME _____

Design your own puzzle.
Write directions for finding the hidden word.
Ask a friend to solve the puzzle.

Use one of the following topics:

A sport   School
Television programs   Your own city or town
Holidays   Famous Americans

REFERENCE REFERRAL

Skills Purpose:
Using Reference Materials

Unit Objectives:
After completing this unit, students should be able to:
1. use the telephone directory to gain information.
2. make meaningful use of the dictionary.
3. select appropriate reference materials to secure specific information.

Preparation & Procedure:
1. Reproduce the activity sheets. Provide the students with pencils, a telephone directory, dictionaries, newspapers, encyclopedias, catalogs, a thesaurus, a cookbook, etiquette books and a driver's manual.
2. Introduce the unit and extend the discussion to focus on instruction for each activity.
3. Let the students work in pairs to complete the activities. Provide guidance and ongoing evaluation as needed.
4. Make provision for filing the completed activities for later referral.

Optional Follow-up Activities:
1. Ask each student to find out the birthdays of the friends he or she listed on page 159 and to write the special date under each name.
2. Instruct the students to write reports about another reference book other than the dictionary. Have the students outline their information as on page 160.
3. Ask each student to make a list of five things that he or she can find in each reference listed on page 161.
4. Have the students use reference books to make up trivia questions for classmates to answer.

NAME _____

Find these words in the puzzle and circle them.

Words to find:

secretary
welder
clerk
mechanic
lawyer
waiter
farmer
electrician
doctor
maid
tailor
mailman
teacher
barber
pilot

m	e	c	h	a	n	i	c	e
a	c	r	w	p	q	d	a	l
i	z	t	a	i	l	o	r	e
d	m	a	i	l	m	a	n	c
d	o	c	t	o	r	x	y	t
l	u	v	e	t	a	c	f	r
a	f	o	r	e	o	l	a	i
w	t	e	a	c	h	e	r	c
y	b	a	r	b	e	r	m	i
e	i	n	g	e	r	k	e	a
r	o	w	e	l	d	e	r	n
s	e	c	r	e	t	a	r	y

List the puzzle words in alphabetical order.
Look up each word in the dictionary and define the occupation.

Using reference materials
© 1989 by Incentive Publications, Inc., Nashville, TN.

*Answer Key

<u>NAME</u>

Write the names of eight friends in alphabetical order.
Use a telephone directory to find their addresses and telephone numbers.
Record the information below.

PERSONAL DIRECTORY

NAME:

The Names of my Friends:	Their Addresses and Phone Numbers:
1.	
2.	
3.	
4.	
5.	
6	
7.	
8.	

Using reference materials
© 1989 by Incentive Publications, Inc., Nashville, TN.

NAME _____

A dictionary is a useful book of and about words. It will tell you what a word means, how to pronounce it, how to use it in a sentence, and how it is spelled.

It is easy to find a word in the dictionary. All of the words are listed in alphabetical order. Two guide words are at the top of each page. The word on the left tells the first word to be found on that page. The word on the right tells the last word on the page.

 There are games that can be played with the dictionary. One game to play with a friend is called the "Word Race." In this game, a word is given and the players see who can find it in the dictionary first. Another game to play is the "Longest Word." Each player opens a dictionary to a page and finds the longest word on the page. Each letter in the word is worth one point. The person with the most points wins the game.

Using the information above, complete the details in this outline.

Reference Books

1. The Dictionary
   A. Uses of the dictionary
      1. _____
      2. _____
      3. _____
      4. _____

   B. Finding words in the dictionary
      1. _____
      2. _____
         a. _____
         b. _____

   C. Dictionary games to play
      1. _____
      2. _____

Using reference materials
© 1989 by Incentive Publications, Inc., Nashville, TN.

NAME _____

Reference Sources:

Atlas   Thesaurus
Dictionary   Encyclopedia
Newspaper   Telephone Directory
Cookbook   Etiquette Book
Store Catalog   Driver's Manual

Which of these reference sources would you use to find information about the following topics?

1. World maps _____

2. The price of a gift _____

3. A person's address _____

4. How to set a table _____

5. The meaning of a word _____

6. Speed limits _____

7. The history of a country _____

8. The pronunciation of a word _____

9. Synonyms and antonyms _____

10. Recipes _____

11. Current events _____

12. Biographies of famous people _____

13. Correct ways to write a letter _____

14. Area codes _____

Using reference materials
© 1989 by Incentive Publications, Inc., Nashville, TN.

*Answer Key

Use the reference sources provided by your teacher to find answers to these questions.

Reference BOOKS

1. What is a kazoo? _____

_____

2. What is the birth date of George Washington? _____

_____

3. How many eggs are required to make a sponge cake? _____

_____

4. What is the capital of Wyoming? _____

_____

5. What is the weather forecast for today? _____

_____

6. What is the area code for Chicago, Illinois? _____

7. What five words are synonymous with *jump* ? _____

_____

8. What states border Idaho? _____

_____

9. What is the longest river in the world and where is it? _____

_____

10. What are the seven continents? _____

_____

_____

Using reference materials
© 1989 by Incentive Publications, Inc., Nashville, TN.

*Answer Key

SCHEDULE SCHEMERS

Skills Purpose:
Making Schedules

Unit Objectives:
After completing this unit, students should be able to:
1. plan a personal time schedule.
2. plan a schedule within the framework of given time blocks.
3. budget time and develop a schedule for completion of a variety of activities.

Preparation & Procedure:
1. Reproduce the activity sheets. Provide the students with pencils, drawing paper, and tempera paint.
2. Verbally introduce the unit.
3. Instruct each student to select two or three friends with whom to discuss the projected schedules.
4. Allow conference time for discussion and evaluation of the completed activities and provide reinforcement as needed.
5. Encourage each student to use the art materials to illustrate a typical day according to one of the schedules developed.

Optional Follow-up Activity:
1. Have the students list the five items that they are supposed to buy (page 166).

Learn to make good use of your time by planning and carrying out schedules.
A good way to begin is by planning for your "free time."
Plan a schedule for this weekend.

FRIDAY MORNING	FRIDAY AFTERNOON
IN SCHOOL	
SATURDAY MORNING	SATURDAY AFTERNOON
SUNDAY MORNING	SUNDAY AFTERNOON

Making schedules
© 1989 by Incentive Publications, Inc., Nashville, TN.

Complete a schedule that you would like for summer camp.
Mark your first, second, and third choices in each category.
Try to balance your schedule with one class from each group and as many of your
    first choices as possible.

1st	2nd	3rd	Class	Time	
			Art and Painting Music Sewing Woodworking	9:00 a.m. - 10:00 a.m. 10:00 a.m. - 11:00 a.m. 1:00 p.m. - 2:00 p.m. 2:00 p.m. - 3:00 p.m.	Arts and Crafts
			Driver Education Cooking Typing Bird Watching Nature Study	10:00 a.m. - 11:00 a.m. 11:00 a.m. - 12:00 noon 1:00 p.m. - 2:00 p.m. 2:00 p.m. - 3:00 p.m. 3:00 p.m. - 4:00 p.m.	Educational
			Tennis Gym Bowling Swimming	9:00 a.m. - 10:00 a.m. 11:00 a.m. - 12:00 noon 2:00 p.m. - 3:00 p.m. 3:00 p.m. - 4:00 p.m.	Sports

Make a camp schedule for a friend.

Time	Class
9:00 a.m. - 10:00 a.m.	
10:00 a.m. - 11:00 a.m.	
11:00 a.m. - 12:00 noon	
1:00 p.m. - 2:00 p.m.	
2:00 p.m. - 3:00 p.m.	
3:00 p.m. - 4:00 p.m.	

Making schedules
© 1989 by Incentive Publications, Inc., Nashville, TN.

Help!! I need another arm!

Make a schedule to help you remember all of these instructions.

Plan your schedule by making notes on the chart below.

Your mother asked you to come home from the ball game at 1:00 p.m. because she has some errands for you to do. She told you that it is very important that you remember to do everything.

At 2:30 p.m. you are supposed to go to the library to return three books. By 3:00 p.m. you should be at the cleaners to pick up your father's suit. Your mother needs some glue and paper, so she asked you to plan to be at the drugstore by 3:30 p.m.

At 4:00 p.m. you are to go to the grocery store to buy bread, milk, and peanut butter. At 5:00 p.m. you are to stop by Mrs. Smith's house to feed the dog and to pick up her mail.

	Time	Where to go	What to do
1.			
2.			
3.			
4.			
5.			
6.			
7.			
8.			
9.			
10.			

Making schedules

SHOPPING CENTER

Skills Purpose:
Problem Solving

Unit Objectives:
After completing this unit, students should be able to:
1. relate analytically to a pictured situation.
2. use written clues to arrive at solutions to specific problems.
3. plan activities on the basis of information gained from following clues.

Preparation & Procedure:
1. If possible, arrange a field trip to a shopping center as motivation. If this is not possible, share a filmstrip, a large picture, or library books featuring a shopping center theme.
2. Reproduce the activity sheets and provide the students with pencils.
3. Verbally introduce the unit and discuss the shopping center directory in as much detail as necessary to give the students a clear understanding of its purpose and use.
4. Extend the discussion to focus on separate activities to enable the students to work as independently as possible.
5. Allow conference time for discussion and evaluation of each completed activity and provide reinforcement as needed.
6. Make provision for sharing the completed activities in a group setting.

Optional Follow-up Activity:
1. Ask each student to imagine that his or her car won't start and that he or she is in parking lot C. Tell the students that they will have to take a bus. Ask the students to determine what is the shortest path to the bus stop (page 168).

Use this shopping center directory to complete pages 169 - 171.

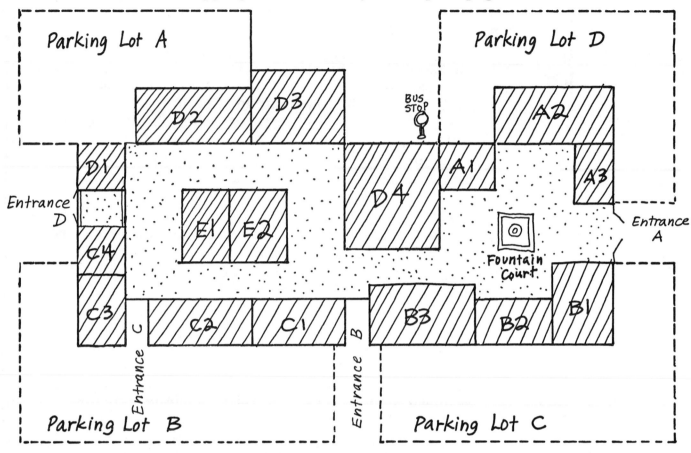

Shopping Center Directory

Clothes
- C-2   Kiddle Clothes Store
- A-3   Mel's Men's Store
- C-3   Jean's Casual Clothes
- B-3   Young Lady Lovely

Food
- D-4   Center Super Market
- E-1   Don's Bakery

Furniture
- A-2   Furniture Mart

Hobby, Pet & Leisure
- C-1   Pal's Pet Store
- E-2   Toys for All Ages
- D-1   Book & Card Nook

Jewelry & Gifts
- C-4   Jim's Gems & Gift Shop

Restaurant
- A-1   Hap's Hamburger Heaven
- D-3   The Fine Diner

Services
- B-2   Beauty & Barber Salon
- D-2   Center Bank & Trust
- B-1   U.S. Post Office

Problem solving
© 1989 by Incentive Publications, Inc., Nashville, TN.

◆ NAME _____

Use the shopping center directory on
  page 168 to find the name of each store
  coded below.
Write the store's name in the blank be-
  neath the picture that best describes it.

1.

E-2._____

2.

A-2._____

3.

C-1._____

4.

E-1._____

5.

A-1._____

6.

D-1._____

7.

B-1._____

A. Use the shopping center directory on page 168 to find out where to go for each item on the shopping list.

Record the name of the store and store code.

THINGS TO DO	NAME OF STORE	STORE CODE
1. Buy a birthday gift.		
2. Buy party clothes.		
3. Buy a birthday card.		
4. Buy ice cream.		
5. Buy grape juice.		
6. Have lunch.		
7. Go to the bank for money.		
8. Buy shoes.		
9. Have a haircut.		
10. Buy a party game.		
11. Buy a birthday cake.		

B. To save time and steps, schedule your shopping day.
Remember, ice cream melts!

9:00 A.M.	Center Bank and Trust	D-2
9:30 A.M.		
10:00 A.M.		
10:30 A.M.		
11:00 A.M.		
11:30 A.M.	(lunch)	
12:30 P.M.		
1:00 P.M.		
1:30 P.M.		
2:00 P.M.	Beauty and Barber Salon	B-2
3:00 P.M.		

Problem solving

Use the shopping center directory on page 168 to solve each of these parking problems.

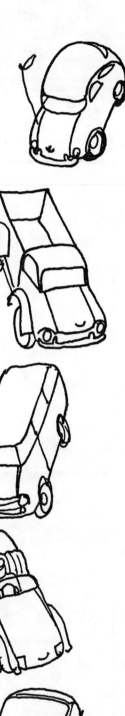

Parking Problem #1

You have to go to the *Furniture Mart* and the *Center Super Market*.

Solution #1 -   You will park in Lot _____ .
You will use Entrance _____ .

Parking Problem #2

You have to go to *Pal's Pet Shop* and *Jean's Casual Clothes*.

Solution #2 -   You will park in Lot _____ .
You will use Entrance _____ .

Parking Problem #3

You have to go to the *U.S. Post Office*, *Toys for All Ages*, and *Fountain Court*.

Solution #3 -   You will park in Lot _____ .
You will use Entrance _____ .

Parking Problem #4

You have to go to *Jim's Gems and Gift Shop*, *The Fine Diner*, and *Young Lady Lovely*.

Solution #4 -   You will park in Lot _____ .
You will use Entrance _____ .

Problem solving
© 1989 by Incentive Publications, Inc., Nashville, TN.

 NAME _____

Design a shopping center of the future and include the kinds of stores
   you would like to shop in twenty years from now.
Label all of the stores and make a shopping center directory.
Refer to page 168 if you need help.

Diagram

Shopping Center Directory

Problem solving
© 1989 by Incentive Publications, Inc., Nashville, TN.

ENRICHMENT
& APPRECIATION

DETAIL DISCOVERY

Skills Purpose:
Detail Awareness

Unit Objectives:
After completing this unit, students should be able to:
1. verbally note likenesses and differences.
2. discover and list common physical likenesses.
3. use descriptive details in personal communication.
4. use listening skills to gather information.

Preparation & Procedure:
1. Reproduce the activity sheets. Gather pencils, art supplies, records and a phonograph. (You may want to have students bring their own records from home.)
2. Vebally introduce the unit.
3. Allow time for discussion and ongoing evaluation of each activity, and provide reinforcement as needed.
4. Encourage the students to use art supplies to add interest to their completed activities.

 NAME _____

Ask a friend to complete this activity with you.
Discuss how the two pictures in each box are the same and how they are different.

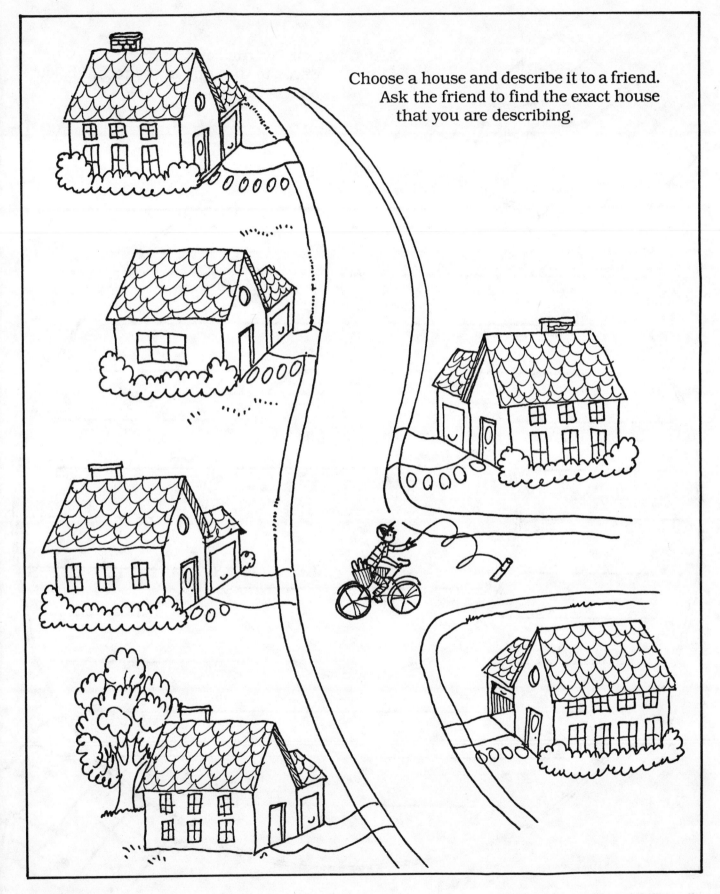

Choose a house and describe it to a friend.
Ask the friend to find the exact house
that you are describing.

Detail awareness
© 1989 by Incentive Publications, Inc., Nashville, TN.

Listen to your favorite song.
Write the words to the song in the record below.

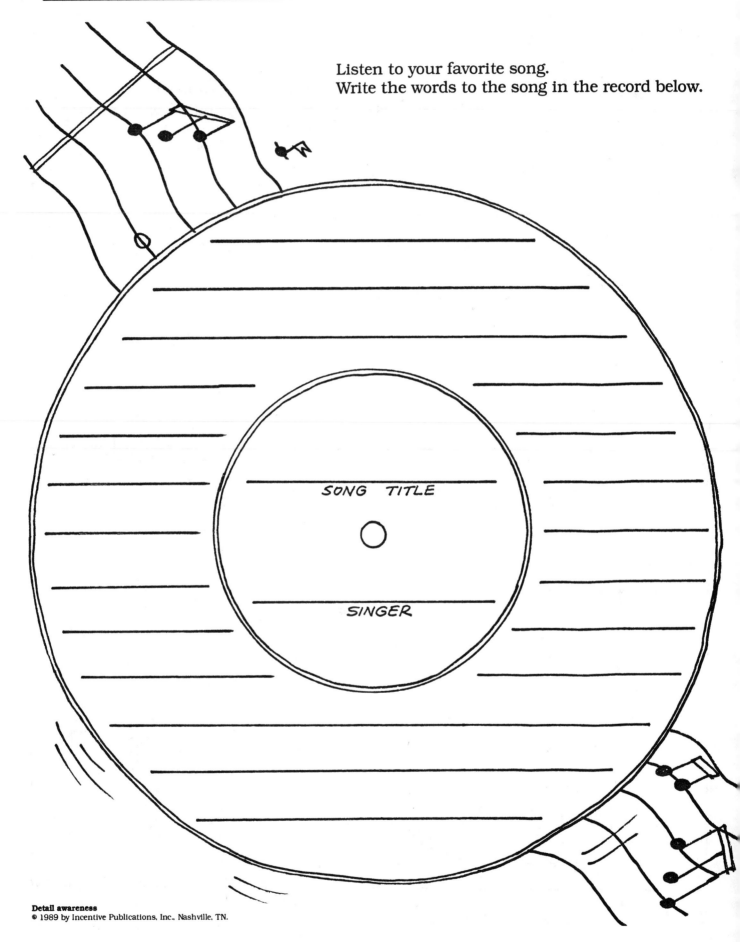

SONG TITLE

SINGER

Draw lines to match the twins.
List three things each set of twins has in common.

Listen to radio or television broadcasts.
"Picture" the programs by completing this questionnaire.

Review a program of your choice.
1. Name of program _____
2. Type of program _____
3. TV or radio station _____
4. Time and date of program _____
5. Summary of story _____
   _____
   _____

Sports Item
1. Game reviewed _____
2. Who played? _____
3. What was the final score? _____
4. What were the outstanding plays? _____
   _____
   _____

News Item
1. Issue (What happened?) _____
2. Who was involved? _____
3. Where did it happen? _____
4. When did it happen? _____
5. Why did it happen? _____
6. How will it affect you? _____
   _____
   _____

Weather Report
1. Forecast for today _____
2. What are the high and low temperatures of the day? _____
3. What was the weather yesterday? _____
4. What is the prediction for tomorrow? _____
   _____
   _____

Commercial
1. What is the product being sold? _____
2. Why are we supposed to buy the product? _____
3. To what group of people does the commercial appeal? _____
4. What did you like about the commercial? _____
5. What did you not like about the commercial? _____
   _____

Detail awareness

HOME SWEET HOME

Skills Purpose:

Idea Association

Unit Objectives:

After completing this unit, students should be able to:
1. associate ideas and pictures.
2. extend ideas into complete thoughts.
3. develop and refine associations to form a creative concept.

Preparation & Procedure:
1. Prepare a large bulletin board with the heading "Home Sweet Home."
2. Reproduce the activity sheets. Provide the students with pencils, dictionaries and art supplies.
3. Verbally introduce the unit.
4. Arrange time for discussion and ongoing evaluation of each activity.
5. Make provision for sharing the completed activity sheets in a small group setting.
6. Ask the students to add creative stories to the bulletin board display. The completed display should stimulate lively classroom discussion and could be used as the focus for creative dramatics, a mural or a poetry collection.

◆ NAME _____

Describe each "home" by telling *who* lives there, *what* it is made of, and *where* it is likely to be located.

Who: _____

What: _____

Where: _____

Who: _____

What: _____

Where: _____

Who: _____

What: _____

Where: _____

Who: _____

What: _____

Where: _____

Who: _____

What: _____

Where: _____

Who: _____

What: _____

Where: _____

Pretend that you are looking in these windows.
Write a sentence describing the people who live in
  each apartment.

_____

_____

_____

_____

_____

_____

Write a paragraph about what you might find if you visited someone living in this house.

_____

_____

_____

_____

_____

_____

_____

_____

_____

_____

Idea association
© 1989 by Incentive Publications, Inc., Nashville, TN.

IMAGI-STATION

Skills Purpose:
Creative Thinking

Unit Objectives:
After completing this unit, students should be able to:
1. express original thoughts.
2. organize creative thinking within a topical framework.
3. develop a creative story with plot and sequence.
4. express personal awareness of differing points of view.

Preparation & Procedure:
1. Reproduce the activity sheets. Provide the students with pencils, crayons, dictionaries and a large scrapbook.
2. Lead a group discussion of the unit and its objectives to encourage creativity. Extend the discussion to focus on separate activities, and provide guidance as needed.
3. Make provision for evaluating and sharing completed activities in a group setting. Encourage each student to select a favorite activity to include in the Imagi-Station scrapbook.

Optional Follow-up Activities:
1. Ask each student to think of a contest that he or she would like to win and to write a story about it.
2. Instruct each student to think of a hero to write a story about and to explain why he or she is a hero.

Name: _____   Name: _____

Age: _____   Age: _____

This girl went to a "super" beauty shop.
Fill in the information for each picture.
Write a paragraph telling how the girl looked "before" and a paragraph telling how
    she looked "after" the "beauty" treatment.

Before _____

_____

_____

_____

_____

_____

_____

After _____

_____

_____

_____

_____

_____

_____

Creative thinking

Write a story about what you would wish for if you were granted two wishes.

JUST TWO!

_____
_____
_____
_____
_____
_____
_____
_____
_____
_____
_____
_____
_____
_____
_____
_____
_____

Creative thinking

Look at the picture and use your imagination to finish the story.

_____I won the pickle eating contest, but_____

_____

_____

_____

_____

_____

_____

_____

_____

_____

_____

_____

_____

_____

_____

_____

_____

Creative thinking
© 1989 by Incentive Publications, Inc., Nashville, TN.

Look at the picture.
Use your imagination to write a
story to go with the last sentence that has been written
for you.
Give your story a title.

_____
Title

_____

_____

_____

_____

_____

_____

_____

_____

_____

_____

_____

_____

_____

_____

I saved the cat, but got stuck in the tree!

Creative thinking
© 1989 by Incentive Publications, Inc., Nashville, TN.

Use this picture, one of these ideas, and your imagination to write a story.

- The score was twelve to twelve. There were only five minutes left in the game . . .
- I picked up the ball and started to run . . .
- I was enjoying the game when all of a sudden . . .
- Boy, was I embarrassed when . . .
- She knew nothing about football . . .

_____
_____
_____
_____
_____
_____
_____
_____
_____
_____
_____
_____
_____

Look at the picture.
Use your imagination to write a
story to go with the last sentence that has been written
for you.
Give your story a title.

_____
Title

_____

_____

_____

_____

_____

_____

_____

_____

_____

_____

_____

_____

_____

_____

_____

_____

I saved the cat, but got stuck in the tree!

Creative thinking
© 1989 by Incentive Publications, Inc., Nashville, TN.

Use this picture, one of these ideas, and your imagination to write a story.

- The score was twelve to twelve. There were only five minutes left in the game . . .
- I picked up the ball and started to run . . .
- I was enjoying the game when all of a sudden . . .
- Boy, was I embarrassed when . . .
- She knew nothing about football . . .

_____

_____

_____

_____

_____

_____

_____

_____

_____

_____

_____

_____

_____

Creative thinking
© 1989 by Incentive Publications, Inc., Nashville, TN.

Write two stories describing two different points of
view concerning what is happening in the picture.

I was on the top of the human pyramid . . .

_____

_____

_____

_____

_____

_____

_____

_____

I was at the bottom of the human pyramid . . .

_____

_____

_____

_____

_____

_____

_____

_____

Write today's horoscope for each zodiac sign.
Then check your forecasts with those given in the newspaper.

 AQUARIUS,
the water bearer

 LEO,
the lion

 PICES,
the fishes

 VIRGO,
the virgin

 ARIES,
the ram

 LIBRA,
the balance

 TAURUS,
the bull

 SCORPIO,
the scorpion

 GEMINI,
the twins

 SAGITTARIUS,
the archer

 CANCER,
the crab

CAPRICORN,
the goat

Creative thinking
© 1989 by Incentive Publications. Inc.. Nashville. TN.

JOB MARKET

Skills Purpose:
Career Awareness

Unit Objectives:
After completing this unit, students should be able to:
1. develop awareness of job demands.
2. express thoughts related to career "fitness."
3. complete a simple job application form.

Preparation & Procedure:
1. Reproduce the activity sheets. Provide the students with pencils, high-interest/low-vocabulary books dealing with various careers, dictionaries, and art supplies.
2. Lead a group discussion focused on different types of occupations and occupational demands.
3. Verbally introduce the unit.
4. Allow time for discussion and ongoing evaluation of each activity, and provide reinforcement as needed.
5. Make provision for filing or sharing the completed activities.

Optional Follow-up Activity:
1. Instruct each student to write a paragraph describing the job responsibilities of the job pictured on page 194.

◆ NAME _____

Draw a picture of yourself at work in a job you would like to have when you are twenty-five years old.

◆ NAME _____

Read the application Joanne filled out for a baby-sitting job.
Think of a job you would like to have, and fill out the application at the bottom of
   the page.

Name: _Marie Joanne Jones_____   Birth date: _1-15-78___

Address: _11 South Road_____   Phone: _222-3333___

Job Applied For: _baby sitter_____

Salary Expected: _$2.00 an hour___   Starting Date: _today____

Educational Background: _Kindergarten-Valentine School_
         _Grades 1-6 - Poke Elementary___

Past Experiences:
   Job   Dates   Why you left
_Baby sitter for Mrs. Smith___ _June 3rd & 5th__ _job over_
Took care of the Brown's dog _Aug. 7th - 13th_ _they returned_
                                                   from vacation
_____

References: _Mrs. Smith_____ _419 South Road___
           _Mrs. Brown_____   _12 Main Street___

Name: _____   Birth date: _____

Address: _____   Phone: _____

Job Applied For: _____

Salary Expected: _____   Starting Date: _____

Educational Background: _____
         _____

Past Experiences:
   Job   Dates   Why you left
_____
_____
_____

References: _____
           _____

Mary is interviewing for a job.
List four reasons why you think she may not get the job.

1. _____

_____

2. _____

_____

3. _____

_____

4. _____

Career awareness
© 1989 by Incentive Publications, Inc., Nashville, TN.

YAK YAK YAK

Bill wants a summer job.
He may have some problems.
Give Bill some suggestions for his next job interview.

_____
_____
_____
_____
_____
_____
_____
_____
_____

Write an advertisement for the "Help Wanted" section of the newspaper for persons needed to fill the following positions:

WANTED: High school football coach; must be _____

_____

_____

_____

_____

WANTED: Good seamstress to work in ladies' specialty dress shop; _____

_____

_____

_____

_____

_____

WANTED: Experienced chef for exclusive restaurant; _____

_____

_____

_____

_____

WANTED: Math tutor for sixth grade student; _____

_____

_____

_____

_____

POP-INS

Skills Purpose:
Vocabulary Development

Unit Objectives:
After completing this unit, students should be able to:
1. enjoy verbal word usage in both sense and nonsense settings.
2. select words to express complete thoughts.
3. complete a story with plot and sequence.

Preparation & Procedure:
1. Reproduce the activity sheets. Provide the students with pencils and art supplies.
2. Discuss the activity sheets and vocabulary in a group setting.
3. Let the students work in pairs to complete the activities and to "check" each other's completed work.
4. Make provision for filing or displaying the completed activities.

Optional Follow-up Activity:
1. Have the students illustrate some part of the story on page 202.

POP-IN WORDS

buzz

bang

HA HA

boo hoo

meow

OUCH

rivet

MOO

cluck

Read these stories to a friend.
Ask your friend to choose pop-in words to make a silly story and then to choose the correct pop-in words to make a story that makes sense.

1. A bee flew by and went "_____."
   If a bee stings me, I'll yell, "_____."

2. When the baby was hot and tired he said,
   "_____."
   His mother gave him a bottle and his funny toy and he said, "_____."

3. A frog sat on a lily pad. "_____,"
   he said. "I wish I were a cow and could say
   '_____,' or a chicken and say
   '_____,' or a cat and say
   '_____.'"

4. The balloon went "_____" when it burst into pieces. I scared the little girl and she cried, "_____."

Vocabulary development
© 1989 by Incentive Publications, Inc., Nashville, TN.

Read these phrases to a friend.
Ask the friend to fill in the missing words.

(a)   To make silly phrases, choose any "pop-in" words.
(b)   To make phrases that make sense, choose the
       correct "pop-in" word for each blank.

"NICE" THINGS TO SAY

1.   "That's such a _____ hat, and you
     look so _____ in it!"
2.   "I really had a _____ time.
     Thank you for being so _____ ."
3.   "That was such a _____ movie.
     I can't wait to tell my _____ friends."
4.   "It's a _____ day. Why don't we
     take a _____ stroll."
5.   "It was so _____ meeting you!"

Read this story with a friend and use the "pop-in" words
   to fill in the blanks.
Make a silly story and one that makes sense.

THE _____ HOUSE

I felt _____ as I opened the
door of the _____ , _____
house. The _____ wind was blowing the
_____ shutters and the moonlight cast
_____ shadows through the
_____ windows.

I don't believe _____ stories about ghosts.
But I know that I heard a _____ howl and
_____ footsteps on the stairs.

I ran out of the _____ door and back to my
own _____ house and hid under my
_____ bed.

POP-IN WORDS

best
haunted
heavy
ugly   nice
squeaky
scary
chilly silly
strange
safe   good
sunny
little
big
pretty
friendly

Vocabulary development
© 1989 by Incentive Publications, Inc., Nashville, TN.

WORD PARTS
TO USE

butter
horse
boy
sun
cakes
slow
nuts
birth
day
break
ball
cow

Some words are made up of two smaller words.
Read this story and fill in the missing word parts.
You may use each word more than once.

This true story was told by an old _____ man

about a lazy cow_____ named _____ poke.

What does a cow _____ do on his birth_____?

_____ poke wakes up at _____rise, hungry

for _____fast. The cook serves him pan_____ ,

_____milk, and dough_____. He goes out

into the _____shine to do his chores. He

sees many _____ flies, pretty yellow

_____cups, and _____boys on _____ back.

His friends yell, "To_____ is your

_____day. Would you like to play base_____ ,

foot_____ or basket_____?" "Since

it's my _____day," the _____boy says,

"I want to play _____ shoes." So, that's what

they do. After a full day, _____poke goes to sleep

at _____ set.

What does a cow _____ do on his birth _____?

Why, he gets a year older!

Vocabulary development
© 1989 by Incentive Publications, Inc., Nashville, TN.

TALL TALES

Skills Purpose:
Creative Expression

Unit Objectives:
After completing this unit, students should be able to:
1. write dialogue to complete a picture story.
2. complete a picture story creatively.
3. write an original story.

Preparation & Procedure:
1. Reproduce the activity sheets and provide the students with pencils and dictionaries. Put the title "A Crazy School Day" near the center of a bulletin board.
2. Verbally introduce the unit.
3. Allow time for discussion and evaluation of each activity, and provide guidance and reinforcement as needed.
4. Make provision for sharing the completed stories in a group setting.
5. Ask the students to add ideas to the bulletin board display.

Optional Follow-up Activity:
1. Have the students write stories about "what will happen when the teacher comes back to school" (page 206).

Write what you think the people are saying in this picture story.

NAME _____

Draw pictures and write dialogue to tell what could happen next in this picture story.

Write a story about the strange things that happened at school the day the teacher was absent.

_____

_____

_____

_____

_____

_____

_____

_____

_____

_____

WHAT'S YOUR LINE?

Skills Purpose:
Dialogue Development

Unit Objectives:
After completing this unit, students should be able to:
1. participate more spontaneously in telephone conversations.
2. express awareness of the dynamics of dialogue.
3. express personal "point of view."

Preparation & Procedure:
1. Reproduce the activity sheets and provide the students with pencils and resource books.
2. Lead a discussion of the importance of clear and concise self-expression.
3. Explain each activity in as much detail as necessary to enable the students to work independently. Encourage the use of resource books for idea clarification and vocabulary suggestions.
4. Plan to give guidance and assistance and to aid in ongoing evaluation.
5. Culminate the unit by involving the students in group discussion and/or creative dramatics.

Create telephone conversations for the situations given below.

SITUATION (The caller's task)	REACTION OF PERSON CALLED (Choose one for each situation)	WHAT NEXT?
1. You are late to dinner . . .	(a) The food is burned and you are angry. (b) You have already eaten.	
2. Invite a friend to a party that is for your best friends only.	(a) You want to go but you are going to another party. (b) You don't want to come.	
3. Call a friend for a homework assignment.	(a) You get the directions mixed up. (b) You didn't get the assignment either, but you don't want to admit it.	
4. Order a birthday cake with green frosting, purple roses, 79 yellow candles, and "Happy Birthday" written in gray icing.	(a) You can't get the directions straight. (b) You don't have any cakes so you try to sell the caller a pie.	
5. You are the teacher and call a parent to talk about his or her child's bad grade.	(a) You are the child and you make excuses as to why the parent can't come to the phone. (b) You are the parent and think the grade is unfair.	

Dialogue development
© 1989 by Incentive Publications, Inc., Nashville, TN.

Choose a topic and take a side.
Are you for or against the statement?
Think of the arguments for your side
of the situation.
One example for each position state-
ment is given.

1. Debate the issue with yourself.
   Think of possible arguments for
   both sides.
2. Debate with a friend.
3. Debate in teams.

SITUATION	POSITION 1 (For)	POSITION 2 (Against)
1. Concrete is better than grass on the playground.	(a) You don't have to cut grass. (b) (c)	(a) If you fall, you'll hurt yourself. (b) (c)
2. Astroturf should be put on the ball field.	(a) It would keep the field dry and free of mud. (b) (c)	(a) You can't run as fast on astroturf. (b) (c)
3. Money should be spent for exploring outer space.	(a) We should discover new frontiers. (b) (c)	(a) Money should be spent for people who are hungry. (b) (c)

Dialogue development
© 1989 by Incentive Publications, Inc., Nashville, TN.

Be a super salesperson!
Try to sell these products to a friend.

Things to include in your SUPER SALES
   PITCH:
1. What the product can do (uses).
2. Why it is worth buying.
3. Why the buyer really needs the
   product.

   More Products to Sell:
   a flat tire
   a bucket with a hole in it
   a pen with no ink
   two left shoes
   play money
   a set of broken dishes
   a burned-out electric light bulb
   a brown sock and a white sock
   a key that has no lock
   a ticket to a play that's over

AN EMPTY BOX

FALSE TEETH

CLOTHES
THAT
DON'T FIT

A LADDER WITH
ONE RUNG

BROKEN
EYEGLASSES

A CAR WITHOUT TIRES

BROKEN TABLE

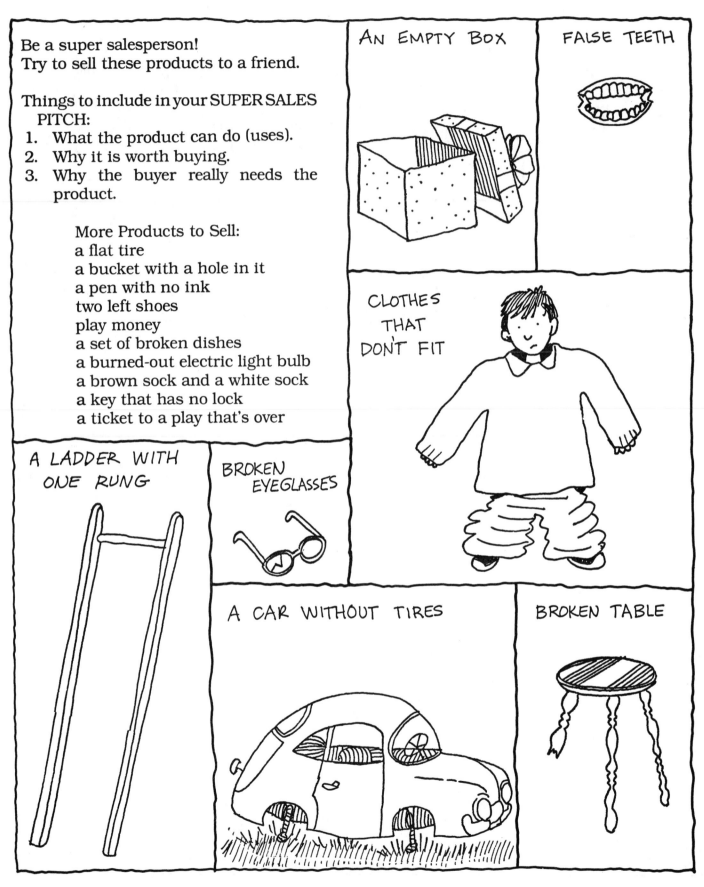

Dialogue development
© 1989 by Incentive Publications, Inc., Nashville, TN.

WORLD OF WORDS

Skills Purpose:
Creative Word Usage

Unit Objectives:
After completing this unit, students should be able to:
1. express awareness of word meanings.
2. use words creatively.
3. develop a story with plot and sequence based on specific word usage.

Preparation & Procedure:
1. Reproduce the activity sheets and provide the students with dictionaries, pencils, construction paper and felt-tip markers.
2. Verbally introduce the unit.
3. Focus individual and group discussion on words being used, and develop chart or chalkboard word lists.
4. Allow time for discussion and ongoing evaluation of each activity.
5. Encourage the students to use construction paper and felt-tip markers to make booklet covers titled "World of Words" for their completed activities.

Write a story using as many of these "B" words as you can.
(For example: A big bee buzzed by Betsy's basket . . .)

More Words to Use:

boy	buy	blue	beautiful	bang	big	buzzing	bright
but	blouse	black	bored	brother	bed	bent	bite
baby	back	book	box	because	bring	brown	by
best	better	birthday	bicycle	bandit	basket	bucket	ball

Write a story using as many
of these "P" words as you
can.
(For example: Patsy planned
a picnic party . . .)

More Words to Use:

party	pen	pass	past	pick	play	pay	pet
pull	pink	pants	paper	pin	pan	pot	purple
plan	plane	pack	prune	pain	pretty	pig	prize

Creative word usage
© 1989 by Incentive Publications, Inc., Nashville, TN.

Write a story using as many of these "T" words as you can.
(For example: An elephant tripped over his trunk and tumbled on his tail . . .)

More Words to Use:

travel	tool	turn	three	ten	trouble	tree	try
table	tiny	truck	tip	top	the	to	them
there	this	that	thin	take	talk	took	today
they	train	thumb	teacher	tomato	toe	tail	town

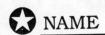

Select one of the following letters and develop your own "letter story" activity sheet.

Be sure to include a giant letter in which you may write a story, illustrations of objects beginning with that letter, and more words to use.

Write a story using as many of the words as you can.

C   R   G   S   K   N   V

More Words to Use:

Review the four stories you have just written.
Select your favorite and illustrate it here.

Title: _____

Make a list of ten words from your chosen story that you know how to spell and
pronounce correctly and that you would like to use in conversation with your
friends.

1. _____   6. _____

2. _____   7. _____

3. _____   8. _____

4. _____   9. _____

5. _____   10. _____

APPENDIX

A WORDY PATH

Find the shortest path from the dogs to the bone.
Write the words found along the shortest path in the blanks below to make a sentence.

_____ _____ _____ .
(noun)   (verb)   (adverb)

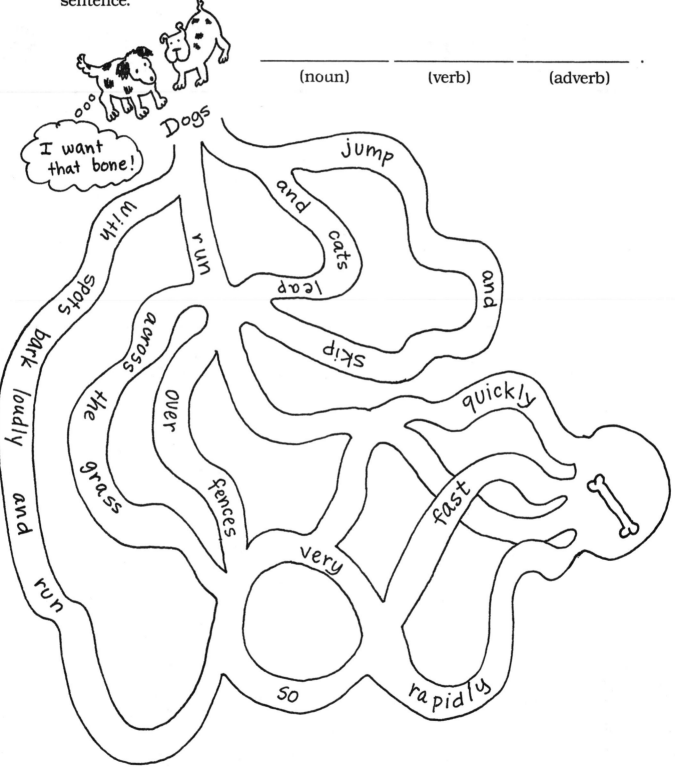

*Answer Key

CROSSWORD CALENDAR

Write the name of each month in the correct
   puzzle box.

Across:
2. The month that comes after May
4. The month that comes before October
5. _ _ _ _ _ showers bring May flowers
8. The hot month right after July
11. The first month of the year
12. The last month of the year

Down:
1. The month for Thanksgiving
3. The month for Valentine sharing
6. The month for Halloween
7. The birthday month of the U.S.A.
9. The flower month before June
10. A very windy month

Months

January
February
March
April
May
June
July
August
September
October
November
December

*Answer Key

CROSSWORD OPPOSITES

Work this crossword puzzle by using words that are opposite in meaning to the words underlined.

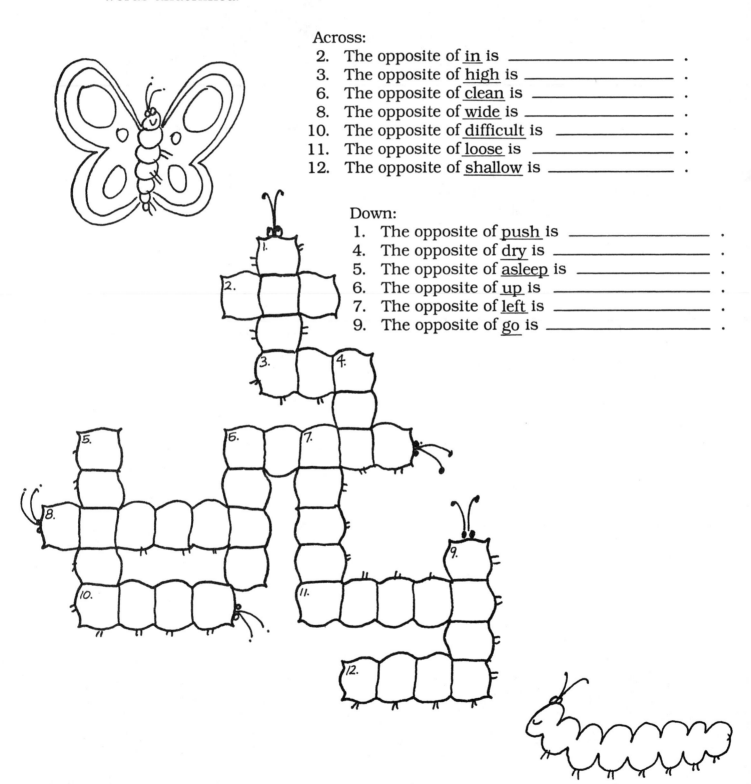

Across:
2. The opposite of <u>in</u> is _____ .
3. The opposite of <u>high</u> is _____ .
6. The opposite of <u>clean</u> is _____ .
8. The opposite of <u>wide</u> is _____ .
10. The opposite of <u>difficult</u> is _____ .
11. The opposite of <u>loose</u> is _____ .
12. The opposite of <u>shallow</u> is _____ .

Down:
1. The opposite of <u>push</u> is _____ .
4. The opposite of <u>dry</u> is _____ .
5. The opposite of <u>asleep</u> is _____ .
6. The opposite of <u>up</u> is _____ .
7. The opposite of <u>left</u> is _____ .
9. The opposite of <u>go</u> is _____ .

*Answer Key

DAFFY DEFINITIONS

Match each definition with a word
from the word box and write the
word in the correct puzzle boxes.

Across:
1. little in size
3. finished
6. too
7. prepared
9. fully satisfied
13. another time
14. unusual
16. not ever
17. no noise
18. to stop

Down:
2. one more
3. as a group
4. to remain in one place
5. where one lives
8. boy child to his parents
10. pleased
11. body in the sky around which
    the earth moves
12. water falling in drops from clouds
15. lovely to look at
17. fast

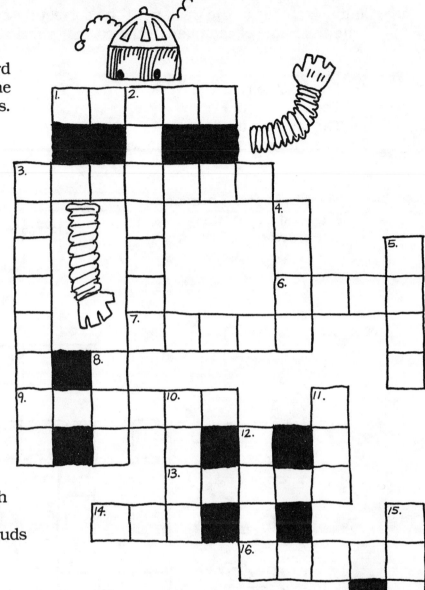

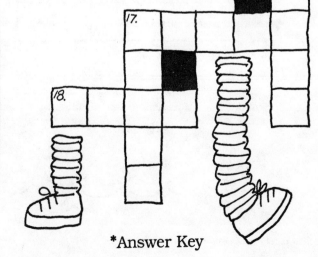

WORD BOX

ready	quiet	never	through
home	quit	also	enough
pretty	quick	another	glad
small	sun	again	odd
stay	son	together	rain

*Answer Key

221

DELIGHTFUL DAYS

Match each day of the week with the correct description.
Write the name of each day in the correct puzzle boxes.

Across:
2. The sixth day of the week
3. The day before Friday
4. The last day of the week
6. The first day of the school week

Down:
1. The day before Thursday
4. The first day of the week
5. The third day of the week

*Answer Key

FIND THE WORDS

Find these words in the puzzle below.
Circle each word.

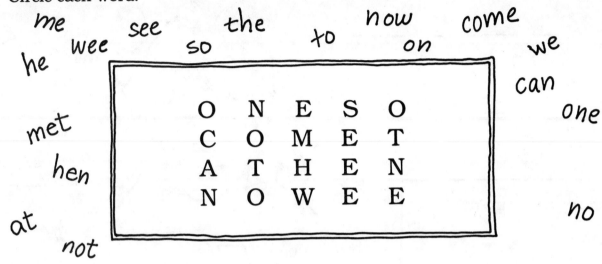

me   see   the   now   come
he wee   so   to   on   we
                                                    can
met   O N E S O   one
           C O M E T
hen   A T H E N
           N O W E E
at   no
  not

Use three or more of the words that you found in the puzzle in a sentence.
Illustrate your sentence.

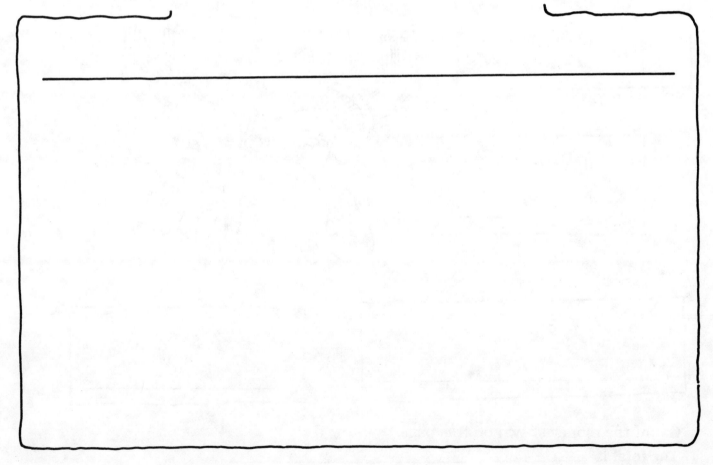

*Answer Key

MONEY MIX-UP

Unscramble the money words in the boxes.
Draw a line from each word to the matching coin or bill.

l i n c e k

_____

r e q r u t a

_____

l d o a r l

_____

i d e m

_____

How much money do I have?

_____

a h l f   o l d l r a

_____

n p e y n

_____

Count the money shown on this page.

The total is _____ .

READY, SET, GO!

Find the word in the word box that completes each statement and write it in the correct puzzle boxes.

Across:

3. Some people wake up early.

   Others wake up _____ .

4. A lemon tastes sour.

   Sugar tastes _____ .

7. A line going up and down is vertical.

   A line going across is _____ .

8. Summer weather is hot.

   Winter is _____ .

9. A giant is big.

   A baby is _____ .

11. A rock is hard.

   A pillow is _____ .

Down:

1. The floor is below.

   The ceiling is _____ .

2. A snail is slow.

   A rabbit is _____ .

4. The ocean is deep.

   A puddle is _____ .

5. You put curtains on a window.

   You put rugs on the _____ .

6. Lifting a book is easy.

   Lifting twenty books is _____ .

10. A brick is heavy.

   A feather is _____ .

WORD BOX		
light	soft	shallow
floor	above	little
difficult	fast	late
horizontal	cold	sweet

*Answer Key

SCRAMBLED SHOPPER

Unscramble the words in the scrambled shopper's list.

Circle the items below that appear on the scrambled shopper's list.

Shopping List

1. SGURA _____
2. AOSP _____
3. KOOB _____
4. DBERA _____
5. PPALE _____
6. EARP _____
7. BMOC _____
8. RUSHB _____
9. CREEAL _____
10. HICKCEN _____
11. ANANABS _____
12. PNEILCS _____
13. TOPTAOES _____
14. MHAMER _____

*Answer Key

SECRET WORD

A. To solve the puzzle, circle all of the hidden words.

try	the
give	no
go	do
going	who
good	hot
how	moo
once	
round	

S	H	G	O	H
G	O	I	N	G
E	W	V	C	O
T	H	E	E	O
R	O	U	N	D
Y	T	M	O	O

B. Find the letters you have not circled in the puzzle.
Unscramble the letters to discover the secret word.

Clue: The pronoun for boy is he.
The pronoun for girl is _____ .

Answer: ___ ___ ___

C. Use the words in the puzzle to fill in the blanks.

1. _____ upon a time, there was a giant.

2. _____ do you do?

3. A circle is _____ .

4. Where are you _____ after school?

5. The opposite of stop is _____ .

6. _____ luck on the test.

7. The opposite of cold is _____ .

8. _____ , you may not use my pencil.

9. _____ me more time.

10. _____ to be quiet.

11. _____ is it?

12. _____ work is done.

13. _____ not run.

14. Cows say _____ .

*Answer Key

SENTENCE SHAPE-UPS

Use these words to fill in the sentence formulas on this page:

Nouns	Verbs	Adjectives	Adverbs	Prepositions	Auxiliary Words
children	run	pretty	quickly	on	the
sidewalk	walk	friendly	loudly	over	an
trees	talk	handsome	quietly	under	a
songs	sing	blue			
birds	fly				

Sentence Formula #1:

_____ .

  (noun)   (verb)

Sentence Formula #2:

_____ .

  (adjective) (noun)   (verb)

Sentence Formula #3:

_____ .

  (noun) (verb)   (adverb)

Sentence Formula #4:

_____ .

  (noun) (verb) (noun)

Sentence Formula #5:

_____ .

  (adjective)   (noun)   (verb)   (adverb)

Sentence Formula #6:

_____ .

  (noun)   (verb) (preposition) (noun)

Sentence Formula #7:

_____ .

  (auxiliary) (noun)   (verb) (preposition) (auxiliary) (noun)

WORD RING-AROUND

Find these words in the puzzle below.
Circle each word.

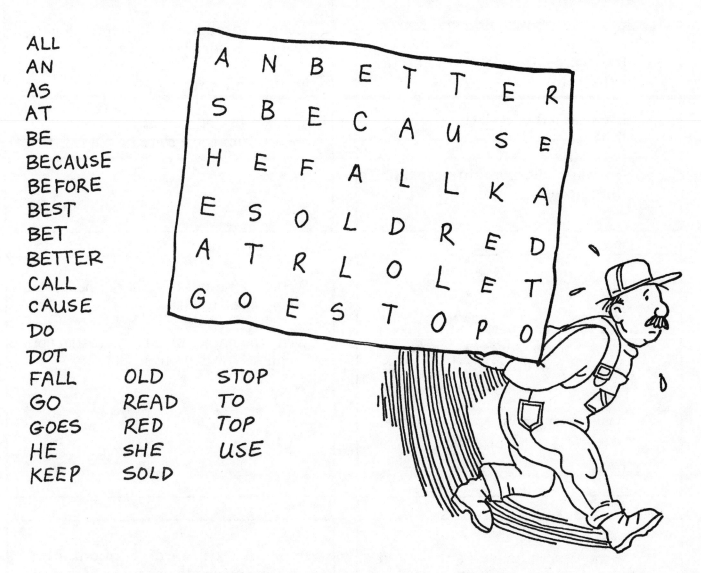

ALL
AN
AS
AT
BE
BECAUSE
BEFORE
BEST
BET
BETTER
CALL
CAUSE
DO
DOT
FALL   OLD   STOP
GO   READ   TO
GOES   RED   TOP
HE   SHE   USE
KEEP   SOLD

Write at least 12 words using only the letters in the word "because."

1.   7.
2.   8.
3.   9.
4.   10.
5.   11.
6.   12.

*Answer Key

24 FIVE-MINUTE SPARKERS
FOR READING & LANGUAGE ARTS

Look in a textbook to find and list:

1. five words that begin with the letter B (b).

2. five words that end with the letter D (d).

3. five words that contain more than three vowels.

Search through the dictionary for the longest word you can find.

Write the word.

Make a list of as many words as you can from the letters in the word.

Be a weatherperson.

Write a weather report for the day.

Tell what the weather was like yesterday.

Give a forecast for tomorrow's weather.

Write the names of all of the people in your classroom.

Write the names of ten objects that you can see from your desk.

Write the descriptions of at least ten things that you can do in the summertime.

List ten things that you cannot do in the summertime.

Draw and write a description of an outfit you would like to wear for each season of the year.

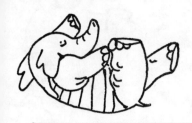

Ask a friend to talk with you about fear.

Write a paragraph about the differences in your fears and your friend's fears.

Write a short paragraph about good manners and when and where to use them.

List as many makes of automobiles as you can.

Compare your list with a friend's list.

Pretend that you are a disc jockey for a local radio station.

Select a few records to be played and write what you will say before playing each record.

Make a list of all of the tools that can be found in a classroom.

Make a list of as many animals as you can.

Divide the list into animals found on the farm, animals found in the jungle, animals found in the home, animals found in the zoo, etc.

Make a list of 20 words that start with the letter "s."

Write a story using these words.

Use this code to find the names coded in the telephone numbers below.

1 2 3 4 5 6 7 8 9 0
R D I H B C F N E A

136-4012
501-5010
719-2239
591-8369
195-9660

Make a schedule for your day tomorrow.

Start with the time you plan to get out of bed.
List other things you want to do and arrange for the time to do them.

Draw a picture of yourself.

Draw a picture of yourself as a baby.

Draw a picture of yourself as you think you will look next year.

Make a list of compound words using color words.

Example: rosebud
Illustrate the word.

Color words to use:

red   pink   white   blue
yellow   rose   black   green

Use a dictionary for extra help!

Write as many words as you can think of that rhyme with these words:

hat   big   can
pot   deep   back
dog   care   tear
jolly   sad   pick

Race with a friend to see who can write the most words in the least amount of time.

Look through a textbook to find:

1. three words that have two e's

2. three words that have two o's

3. three words that have two l's

Write the words.

Write a menu for a fancy restaurant that you would like to own.

Design a cover for the menu.

Draw a picture of the outside of the restaurant and arrange a window display to attract customers.

List at least three things that you like about school.

List at least three things that you dislike about school.

Write a story about a "perfect day at school" which includes all of the things you like and none of the things you dislike.

Write a script for a television special honoring the principal of your school.

Be sure to include events about the principal's past and present life and about his or her hopes for the future of the school.

Write sentences using these prepositions.

to   by   up
of   upon   around
after   over   in

Write a paragraph describing a game or sport.

Ask a classmate to guess what the sport is.

READING RECORD

Title of Book	Date Finished	Number of Pages Read	What I Liked or Disliked Most About The Book
1.			
2.			
3.			
4.			
5.			
6.			
7.			

STUDENT INTEREST INVENTORY

Name _____ Date _____

1. The subject that I like best is _____ .

2. I like this subject because _____
_____ .

3. The subject that I like least is _____ .

4. I like this subject least because _____
_____ .

5. The thing I like best about school is _____
_____ .

6. If I could make one change in my school, I would change _____
_____ .

7. I like to read books about _____ .

8. During my free time I like to _____
_____ .

9. If I could change one thing about myself, I would change _____
_____ .

10. The person I admire most is _____ .

11. I admire this person because _____
_____ .

12. Something unique about me is _____
_____ .

Other KIDS STUFF™ Books for Middle Grades Language Arts and Reading

Edwards, Candy. **The Reference Point.** 1983.
- a collection of reproducible pages, learning centers & teaching suggestions that help develop and strengthen important library skills.

Forte, Imogene. **Library & Reference Bulletin Boards.** 1986.
- motivational bulletin boards with patterns and additional captions.

Forte, Imogene. **Read About It Middle Grades.** 1982.
- reproducible activities which focus on word recognition, word usage and independent reading skills.

Forte, Imogene. **Think About It Middle Grades.** 1981.
- reproducible activity sheets designed to develop thinking skills such as discovering, predicting, inventing, interpreting, imagining and more.

Forte, Imogene. **Write About It Middle Grades.** 1983.
- reproducible work sheets which focus on vocabulary development, technical writing, composition and original writing.

Forte, Imogene & Pangle, Mary Ann. **Reading Bulletin Boards.** 1986.
- skills-based boards with activities to supplement daily reading programs.

Frank, Marjorie. **Complete Writing Lessons for the Middle Grades.** 1987.
- 30 complete writing lessons & accompanying reproducible student activity sheets.

Frank, Marjorie. **If You're Trying To Teach Kids How To Write, You've Gotta Have This Book.** 1979.
- a how-to book for understanding and working with the whole writing process with ideas for specific activities & suggestions for solving writing problems.

Reading Yellow Pages (by The KIDS' STUFF People). 1988.
- timesaving reading-related lists & ideas.

Richards, Joanne & Standley, Marianne. **One For The Books.** 1984.
- original & creative ways to present book reports.

Richards, Joanne & Standley, Marianne. **Write Here.** 1984.
- includes writing activities, bulletin boards & suggestions for motivating students.

Writing Yellow Pages For Students & Teachers (by The KIDS' STUFF People). 1988.
- timesaving writing lists such as synonyms, prefix & suffix meanings, spelling helps, editing checklists, capitalization & punctuation rules, story starters & more.

ANSWER KEY

Pg. 14   1. cup 2. ripe 3. Bake 4. hot 5. Roast 6. Heat 7. egg 8. ham 9. Use 10. milk

Pg. 15   1. bag, pan, can 2. pen, bell 3. fish, lid, milk 4. pop, box, pot 5. butter, cup, syrup

Pg. 16   A. 1. mist, most or must 2. pretty 3. say or soy 4. this or thus 5. ham, hem, him or hum 6. shaw or show 7. old 8. we 9. am 10. brawn or brown 11. black or block 12. white 13. her 14. much 15. jump 16. hid 17. carry 18. long or lung 19. hurt 20. ham, hem, him or hum 21. two 22. be 23. or 24. walk 25. bring or brung 26. kind 27. what or whit 28. them 29. try 30. help 31. step or stop 32. he, hi or ho 33. up

B. 1. new, now 2. saw, sew, sow 3. want, went 4. wash, wish 5. thank, think, thunk 6. at, it 7. wall, well, will 8. bat, bet, bit, bot, but 9. get, got, gut 10. tap, tip, top 11. ham, hem, him, hum 12. as, is, us 13. cat, cot, cut 14. fall, fell, fill, full 15. grew, grow 16. an, in, on 17. pat, pet, pit 18. far, fir, for, fur 19. held, hold 20. tan, ten, tin, ton, tun 21. bag, beg, big, bog, bug 22. shall, shell 23. wan, win, won 24. ma, me, my

Pg. 28   1. unhappy, crying, sad 2. pleased, happy, glad 3. sly, sneaky, shifty 4. tired, bored, sleepy 5. blushing, shy, bashful 6. questioning, wondering, thinking 7. surprised, shocked, frightened 8. angry, furious, annoyed

Pg. 33   A. 1. to 2. two 3. too
B. 1. to, to, two 2. to
3. too, to 4. two, two, to

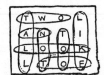

Pg. 40   (Top Puzzle) Across: 2. brought 5. found 6. led 7. were 8. paid Down: 1. sold 3. got 4. told 7. wept
(Bottom Puzzle) Across: 1. took 3. ate 5. was 7. came 8. did 10. ran Down: 2. knew 3. asked 4. used 6. gave 9. drank

Pg. 42   Across: 3. book 5. ball 6. bird 7. pencil 9. car 10. bear Down: 1. table 2. horse 4. girl 5. boy 8. chair

Pg. 43   1. you 2. his 3. mine
4. them 5. she 6. this 7. he
8. they 9. I 10. hers 11. it
Note: 2 it's, 3 I's, & 4 he's may be found

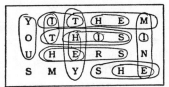

Pg. 44   (Top Puzzle) Across: 1. I 2. they 5. us 7. we Down: 1. It 3. he 4. you 6. she
(Bottom Puzzle) Across: 2. my 4. our 6. their 7. his Down: 1. her 3. your 5. its

Pg. 49   Across: 2. cheerful 4. action 7. backward 9. kindness 11. helpless 12. question
Down: 1. clearly 3. forward 5. thoughtful 6. darkness 8. careless 10. sweetly

Pg. 50   1. payment 2. drainage 3. frontward 4. clearly 5. allowance, allowed, allowable, allowing 6. armor, arming 7. cheerful, cheerless, cheering 8. caring, careless, careful 9. helping, helpful, helped, helpless, helper 10. wishful, wishing, wished 11. collection, collected, collectable, collectible, collective, collector, collecting 12. action, active, acting, acted, actor, actable 13. question, quester 14. likeable, liked, likely, liker, likeness, liking 15. reality, really 16. effective, effecter 17. fruitful, fruiter, fruitless, fruitage 18. ailment, ailing 19. fixable, fixity, fixing, fixed 20. sweetness, sweetly, sweeting

Pg 56:   1. distrust, mistrust, entrust 2. preview, review 3. bicycle, recycle 4. delay, relay, mislay 5. intend, pretend, contend, distend, extend 6. displace, replace, misplace 7. enlarge 8. enjoy 9. ingrown 10. excite, incite, recite 11. reclaim, proclaim, disclaim, exclaim 12. reform, inform, conform, deform, preform 13. dislike, unlike 14. misfit, refit, unfit 15. intake, mistake, retake 16. nonsense 17. prevent, convent, invent 18. depart 19. enforce 20. contract, detract, distract, protract, retract

Pg 59:   Across: 1. dish 3. wag 4. can 6. coat 7. fix 8. fell 9. money
Down: 1. dog 2. hen 3. wing 4. cat 5. mouse 7. floor 8. five

Pg. 60:   1. făt, căt, săt, hăt, flăt, thăt, făt, căt, hăt 2. Dăn, plăn, făn 3. măd, săd; sănd, lănd

Pg. 61:   1. kĭng, rĭng, sĭng, thĭng, kĭng, sĭng 2. wĭtch, stĭtch; (broom, room) 3. bĭg, wĭg, pĭg; fĭt, bĭt

Pg. 62:   1. (tĕn), (mĕn) tĕnt, wĕnt, rĕnt; shĕd, bĕd 2. (Rŏb) (jŏb) Pŏp, shŏp, mŏp; sōda, someōne, bŏy

Pg. 66:   buttercup, butterfly, buttermilk, storehouse, storeroom, classmate, classroom, shoeblack, shoehorn, newsboy, newsman, newspaper, blackberry, blackboard, blackmail, mushroom, bedbug, horseshoe, horseman, flypaper, milkman, schoolboy, schoolhouse, schoolman, schoolmate, schoolroom, strawberry, strawboard, ladybug, paperboard, paperboy, salesman, salesroom, cupboard, cupcake, pancake, cowberry, cowboy, cowman, mailbox, mailman, sandbox, sandman, sandpaper, boxberry, boxboard, rainfall, rainwater, firebox, firebug, firefly, firehouse, fireman, firewater, houseboy, housefly, houseman, houseroom, backboard, backfire, backhouse, backwater

Pg. 70: Across: 2. pants 4. coat 5. dress 7. shirt 8. blouse 11. apron 12. jacket
Down: 1. hat 3. socks 6. skirt 7. shoe 8. belt 9. sweater 10. glove

Pg. 71: 1. rooms 2. fruits 3. clothes 4. holidays 5. colors 6. furniture 7. animals 8. sports

Pg. 74: 1. fictional characters 2. countries 3. modes of transportation 4. states 5. tools 6. weather words 7. moods
8. things that measure 9. occupations

Pg. 89: Sandy wants to buy a roller skate.

Pg. 96:
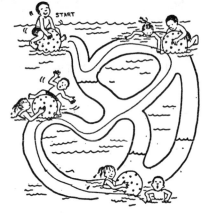

Pg. 103: 1. Tell the story to the sleepy baby. The baby will go to bed. 2. The sleepy little cat walked back home with the sleepy big cat. 3. The milkman gave the milk to the woman. The woman gave the milk to the cat.

Pg. 104: The big man walked to the store to buy milk for the little baby. The man walked up the stairs and down the stairs. The man walked down the straight road and the curved road. The man bought the milk and walked back down the road and climbed the stairs to the house. The man gave the little baby the milk. The little baby was sleepy. The big man was sleepy. Can you tell why?

Pg. 112: 1. first successful airplane flight, Dec. 17, 1903
2. first flight across Atlantic, May 21, 1927
3. Neil Armstrong lands on the moon, July 20, 1969
4. first operational jets introduced, 1945
5. jet age introduced to civilians, 1950s
6. Americans & Russians orbit earth together, July 1975

Pg. 116: Across: 2. green 3. brown 7. pink 8. red 9. purple Down: 1. yellow 3. black 4. orange 5. white 6. blue

Pg. 118: 1. atlas 2. mountain 3. roads 4. gasoline 5. South America 6. Mexico City 7. coming 8. girl

Pg. 124:

Pg. 131: Note: 2 no's, 4 a's & 2 at's may be found

Pg. 142:   Wed., Sept. 8
Dear Mary,
    I'm going to have a party on Friday, September 10 at four o'clock. Will you be able to come?
    I talked to Jim and he said, "I would love to come to the party!"
    I think that a lot of people will be there. I hope that you will be there too!
    I'll be anxious to hear your reply.
                              Sincerely,
                              Charlie

Pg. 144:
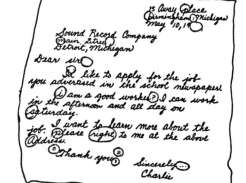

Pg. 149: Mystery Car Ride #1: movie theater/see a movie
Mystery Car Ride #2: cafe/eat

Pg. 152:
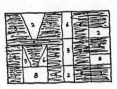

Pg. 153:

Pg. 154:

Pg 155:

Pg. 158:
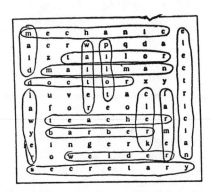

Pg. 161: 1. atlas 2. store catalog 3. telephone directory 4. etiquette book 5. dictionary 6. driver's manual 7. encyclopedia 8. dictionary 9. thesaurus 10. cookbook 11. newspaper 12. encyclopedia 13. etiquette book 14. telephone directory

Pg. 162: 1. a toy musical instrument that makes a humming noise 2. February 22, 1732 3. will vary 4. Cheyenne 5. will vary 6. 312 7. leap, hop, spring, bound, skip 8. Washington, Oregon, Nevada, Utah, Wyoming, Montana 9. Amazon, South America 10. Africa, Antarctica, Asia, North America, South America, Europe, Australia

Pg. 218: Dogs run quickly.

Pg. 219: Across: 2. June 4. September 5. April 8. August 11. January 12. December
Down: 1 November 3. February 6. October 7. July 9. May 10. March

Pg. 220: Across: 2. out 3. low 6. dirty 8. narrow 10. easy 11. tight 12. deep
Down: 1 pull 4. wet 5. awake 6. down 7. right 9. stop

Pg. 221: Across: 1. small 3. through 6. also 7. ready 9. enough 13. again 14. odd 16. never 17. quiet 18. quit
Down: 2. another 3. together 4. stay 5. home 8. son 10. glad 11.sun 12. rain 15. pretty 17. quick

Pg. 222: Across: 2. Friday 3. Thursday 4. Saturday 6. Monday Down: 1. Wednesday 4. Sunday 5. Tuesday

Pg. 223:

Pg. 225: Across: 3. late 4. sweet 7. horizontal 8. cold 9. little 11. soft
Down: 1 above 2. fast 4. shallow 5. floor 6. difficult 10. light

Note: 2 no's may be found

Pg. 226: 1. sugar 2. soap 3. book 4. bread 5. apple 6. pear 7. comb 8. brush 9. cereal 10. chicken 11. bananas 12. pencils 13. potatoes 14. hammer

Pg. 227: A.
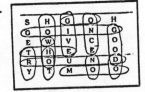

B. she
C. 1. Once 2. How 3. round 4. going 5. go 6. Good 7. hot 8. No 9. Give 10. Try 11. Who(or how) 12. The 13. Do 14. Moo

Pg. 229: Note: 2 all's, 3 be's, 2 he's & 3 to's may be found
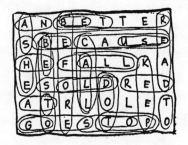